THE WORLD OF

Geography

CLIVEDEN PRESS

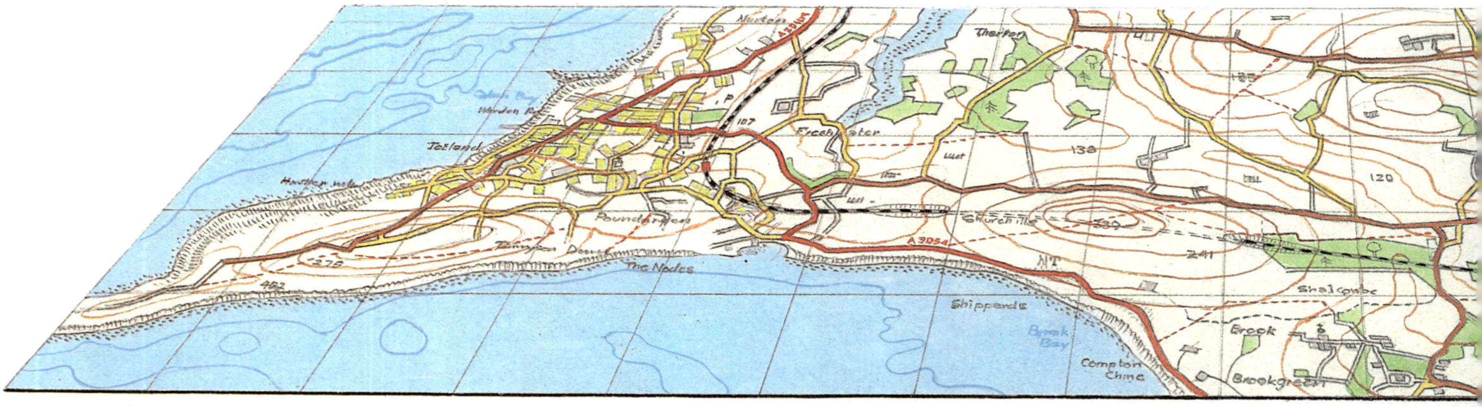
Totland
Poundgreen
The Nodes
A3054
138
120
241
NT
Shippards
Brook
Brookgreen
Compton
Chine

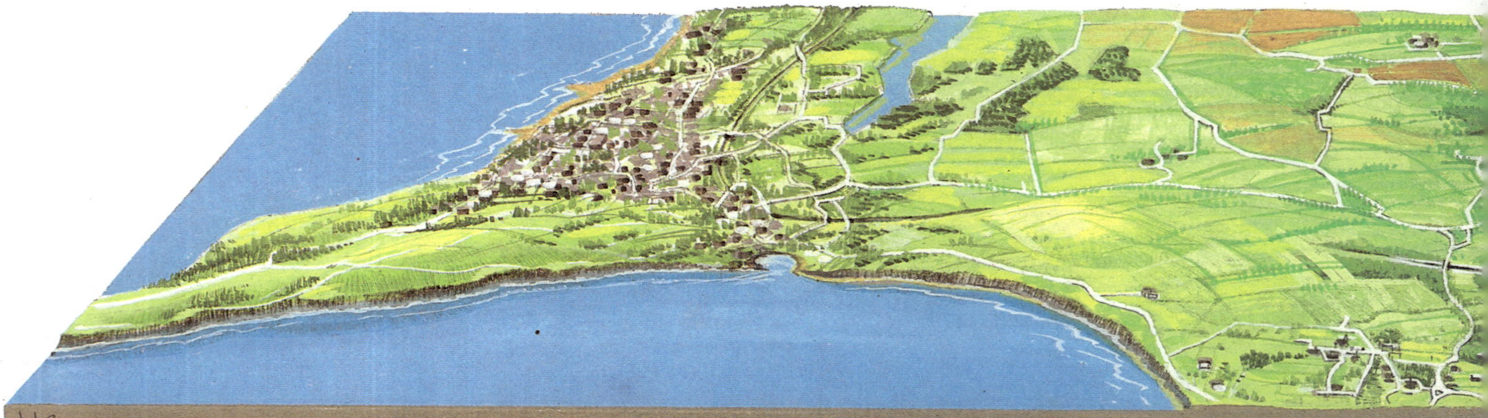

Contents

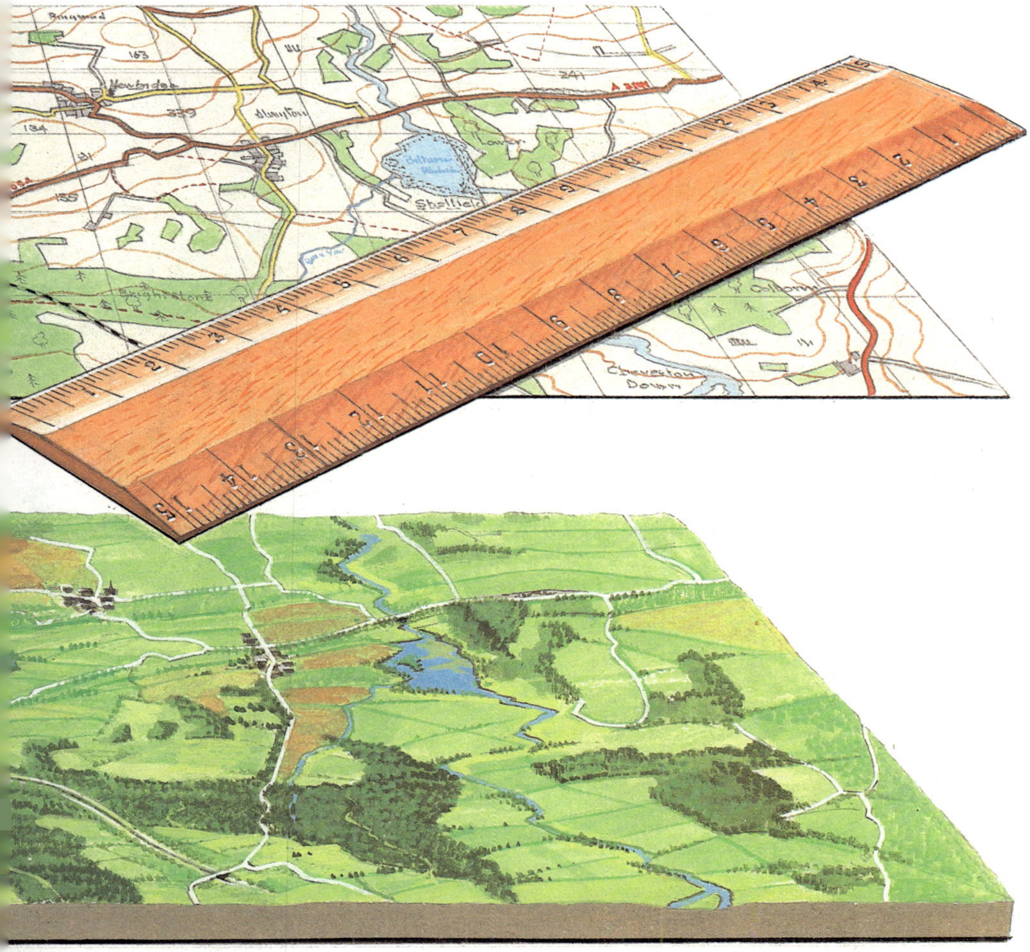

Birth of the Earth

Most scientists now agree that the Earth was formed from a cloud of gas and dust. This cloud was drifting through space about 5000 million years ago. Gradually, more and more particles were drawn to the centre by gravity. There, about 4600 million years ago, they formed a star, the Sun. The material left over formed the planets, moons and other bodies that make up the Solar System

Above: The Earth is made up of three parts. The thin crust varies between 60-70 km thick under the highest montains to about 5 km thick under the oceans. Beneath the crust is the denser (heavier) mantle. The mantle is about 2900 km thick. It encloses the extremely dense core, which measures about 6920 km across. The inner core is solid, but the outer core is probably liquid.

The Earth's Early History

The youthful Earth was probably a huge ball of gas, rather like Jupiter or Saturn. But eventually, because of gravity, heavier elements, notably iron, sank towards the centre, forming a dense core, while lighter elements stayed near the surface. As a result, the Earth now has a very dense (heavy) core, made up largely of iron and nickel, a dense mantle and a relatively light crust.

The Earth slowly shrank into the rocky planet we know today. At first, the surface was hot and molten. Geologists have not found any rocks much older than about 3800 million years, although the Earth itself is about 4550 million years old. Rocks formed in the first 700 million years were probably all broken up and remelted.

The Earth's first atmosphere was poisonous, but it contained water vapour released from the rocks by volcanoes. It contained little oxygen, the gas we need to breathe. The oxygen content began to increase about 1900 million years ago, when oxygen-producing plants first developed.

Below: For many millions of years after its formation, the Earth's surface must have been blazing hot. Constant volcanic activity released gas and water vapour from the rocks inside the Earth. The gases formed a primitive and poisonous atmosphere. Later on, when the surface started to cool, there were great thunderstorms. Rain started to fill up hollows in the early crust. It was perhaps in these warm pools that the first living things, bacteria, appeared.

THE EARTH'S DIMENSIONS

DIAMETER: The equatorial diameter is 12,756 km, but the polar diameter is shorter, 12,713 km.

CIRCUMFERENCE: The equatorial circumference (the distance around the equator) is 40,075 km. But if you travel around the Earth via the poles (the polar circumference), the distance is only 40,007 km.

AREA: The Earth has an area of 510,066,000 km².

LAND AND SEA: The oceans cover 361,740,000 km². This is nearly 71 per cent of the Earth's surface.

Ages of the Earth

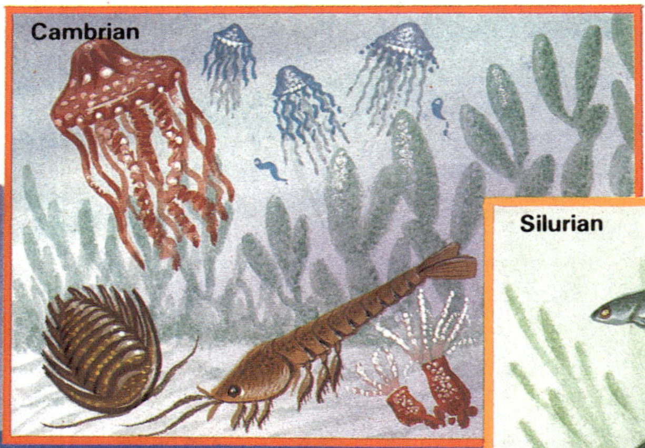

Left: Invertebrates (animals without backbones), including jellyfishes and trilobites, were common in the Cambrian period. Vertebrates (fishes) appeared near the end of the Cambrian period.

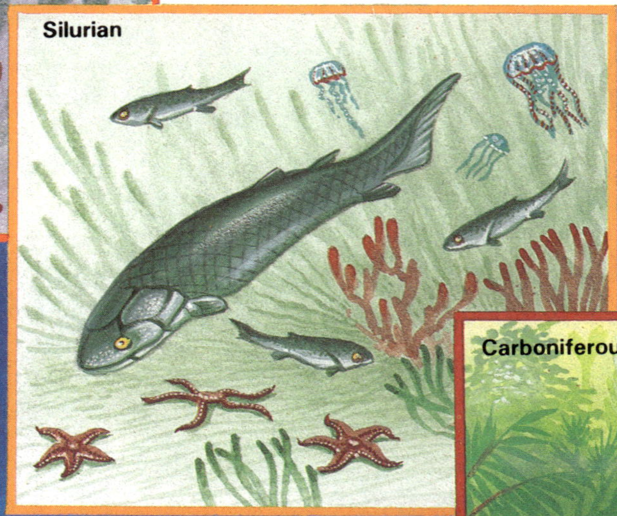

Left: Armoured fishes abounded in the Silurian period, when the first land plants evolved.

Below: The earliest reptiles appeared in the Carboniferous period. Many lived in swamps. Buried swamp plants were slowly turned into layers of coal.

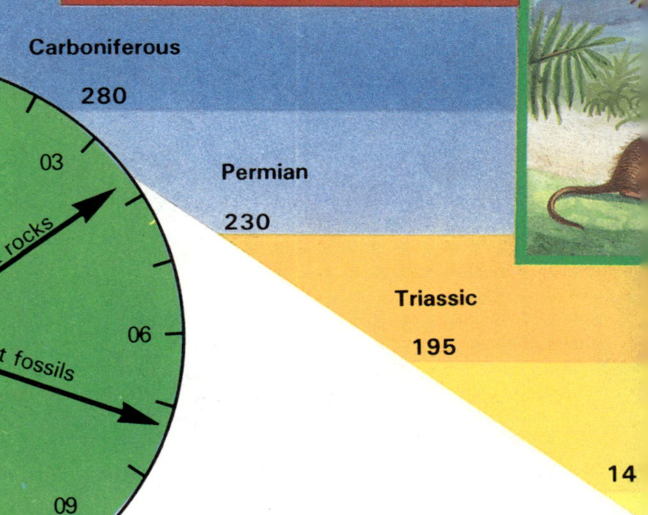

Above: A chart of the geological periods of the Earth's history and the evolution of life forms. The numbers represent how long ago (in millions of years) each period began.

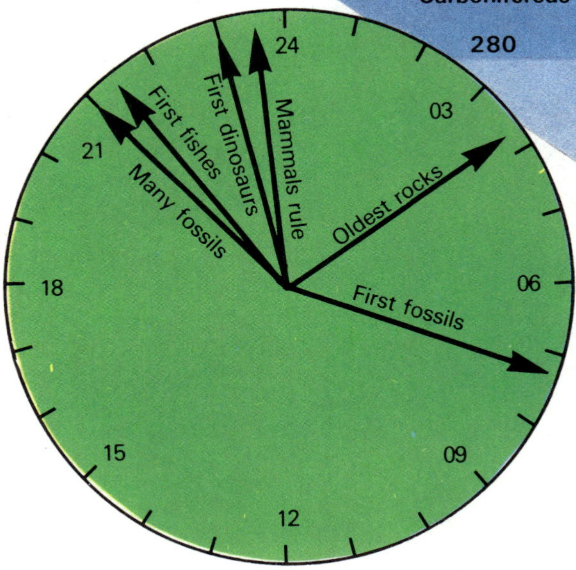

Right: One way to appreciate the vast time span of Earth history is to imagine it being compressed into 24 hours. We can only guess what happened during the first 3 hours 44 minutes, because no rocks formed in the first 700 million years of Earth history have yet been discovered.

The oldest known fossil was formed at 07.28 on our 24-hour clock, although simple living things, such as bacteria, probably existed long before this. But fossils are rare until about 21.00 hours, the start of the Cambrian period.

The first vertebrates (animals with backbones) were fishes. They appeared at 21.20. The first amphibians appeared at 22.10 and the first dinosaurs at nearly 23.00. The dinosaurs died out at 23.29, leaving the way open for mammals. And when did modern people appear? Less than a second before midnight.

Dating Rocks

The study of fossils made possible the fixing of the relative ages of rocks. And in the early 20th century, the discovery of radioactivity enabled scientists to fix the absolute ages of rocks. This is because some rocks contain bits of radioactive material which decays, or breaks down, at a fixed rate. Therefore, when scientists measure the proportion of a radioactive substance that has decayed, they can establish its age.

Eras and Periods

The last 570 million years are divided into the Palaeozoic (ancient life), Mesozoic (middle life) and Cenozoic (recent life) eras.

The Palaeozoic era (570-230 million years ago) is divided into six periods, although US geologists divide the Carboniferous period into two: the Mississippian and Pennsylvanian periods. The first period of the Palaeozoic era is the Cambrian. Cambrian rocks are rich in fossils. But in Precambrian rocks, formed before the Cambrian period began, fossils are rare. The Palaeozoic era saw the appearance of the first vertebrates (fishes), amphibians and reptiles.

The Mesozoic era (230-65 million years ago), contains three periods. It saw the rise of reptiles, including huge dinosaurs. Most reptiles became extinct at the end of the era.

The Cenozoic era in the last 65 million years saw the rise of mammals. This era contains two periods: the Tertiary and the Quaternary. Mighty mountain ranges such as the Alps and Himalayas were born during this era.

Above: The British Isles would look like this if the sea level rose or if the land sank by only 60 metres. The land and sea have changed many times throughout Earth history.

Left: The first dinosaurs appeared in the Triassic period. The first mammals also evolved at this time.

Below left: The Jurassic period saw the emergence of such dinosaurs as *Brontosaurus* and *Stegosaurus*. There were flying reptiles, called Pterosaurs, and the first bird, *Archaeopteryx*.

Below: The Tertiary and Quaternary periods were dominated by mammals, such as giant ground sloths, huge grazing animals, sabre-toothed tigers and many birds. Primates date back 60 million years. Modern people (who are primates) appeared about 50,000 years ago.

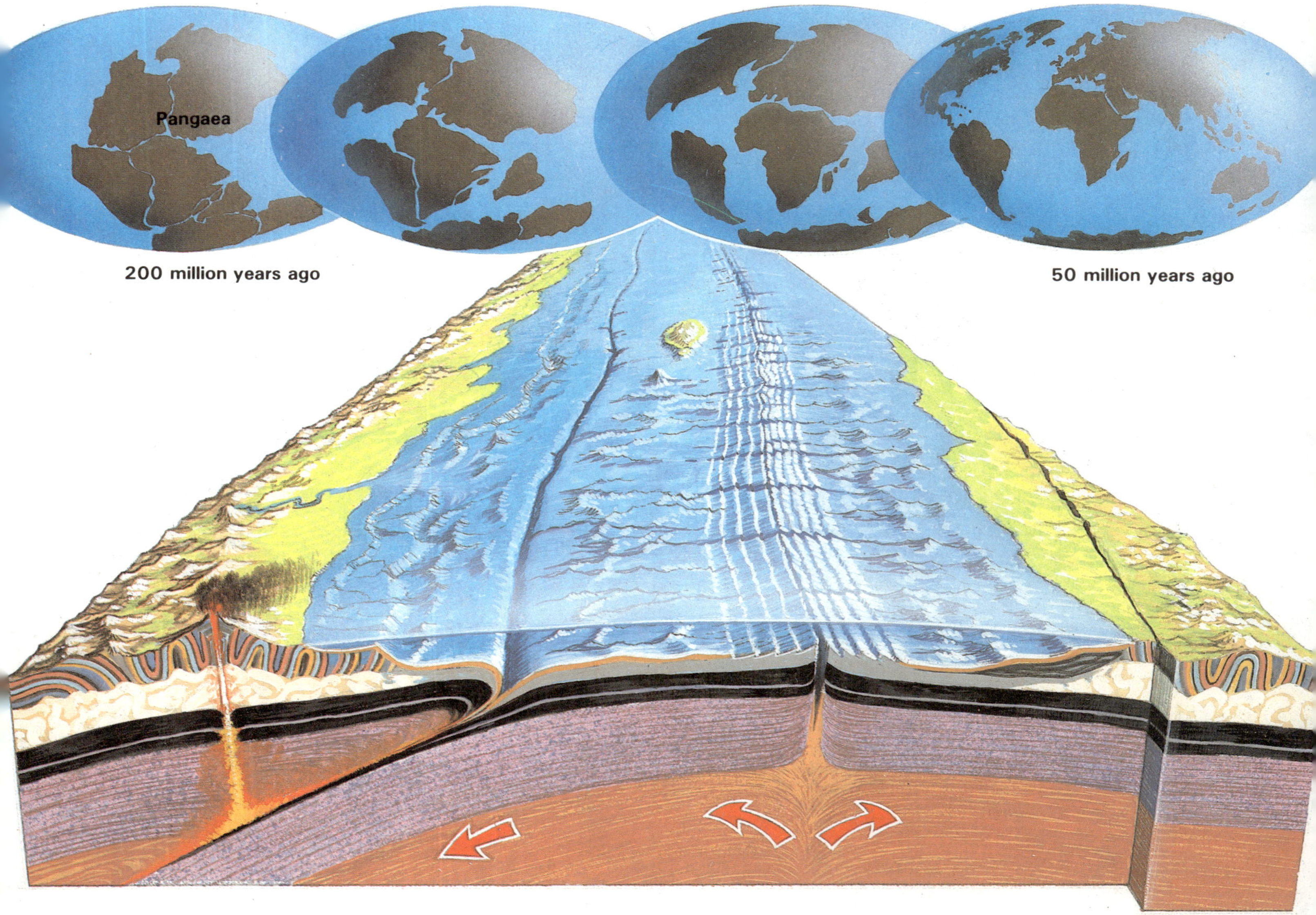

The Earth Beneath

Top: the maps show how the world has changed over the last 200 million years.

Above: The diagram shows an ocean ridge rising from the sea floor. In the centre of these ridges are valleys. These valleys are the edges of plates. Semi-molten material in the upper mantle is rising beneath the ridges. Under the plates it divides and flows sideways, pulling the plates apart. As the plates move, molten material wells up to fill the gap. It hardens into new crustal rock.

Along the deep ocean trenches, the fluid material sinks dowards and one plate is pushed beneath another. The diagram shows plates moving apart and plates colliding. Other plates move alongside each other. Such plates are separated by cracks called transform faults.

Look at a map of the Atlantic Ocean. You will see that North and South America look as though they would fit together with Europe and Africa, like pieces in a jigsaw. About 70 years ago, some scientists suggested that the continents were once joined together.

A German, Alfred Wegener (1880-1930), found similar rock structures on the edges of the facing continents. Fossils of the same land animals, which lived around 200 million years ago, were dug up in South America and Africa. How did they get there? They could not have swum the ocean. Wegener was convinced that the continents had been joined together 200 million years ago. But how do continents move?

Ocean Ridges and Trenches

The study of the oceans in recent years has helped to explain how continents move. No rocks in the oceanic crust are much older than 200 million years. This shows that the oceans are young features, unlike the continents, which have rocks dating back 3800 million years. The youngest rocks are in the middle of long, mostly underwater mountain ranges, or ocean ridges. The rocks in the crust become progressively older away from the ridges in both directions. The ocean ridges are earthquake zones. Earthquakes also occur along the deep ocean trenches, near the edges of the oceans.

Moving Plates

Boundaries between large blocks in the Earth's surface, called plates, run through the ocean ridges. Plates consist of the thin crust, including the continents, and part of the upper mantle. Under the ridges, hot fluid material is rising in the mantle and spreading sideways beneath the plates. These movements are pulling the plates apart by 1 to 10 cm a year. When the plates move, molten material rises to plug the gaps. It then hardens into new crustal rock.

Along the ocean trenches, however, plates are colliding and one plate is being pushed down beneath another. As it descends, the front edge of the plate is melted. Some plates move apart and some collide with each other. A third kind of movement occurs when plates move alongside each other. They move along long cracks in the surface, called transform faults.

THE EARTH'S CHANGING FACE

A space traveller passing the Earth 200 million years ago would have seen one large landmass and one vast blue ocean. But around 135 million years ago, the landmass, called Pangaea, had started to break up and the pieces were slowly drifting apart. The modern oceans were created between them. Some plates were large. Others, like the one carrying what is now India, were smaller. The Indian plate had been attached to Africa. But around 50 million years ago, it was pushing against the large Eurasian plate. Between the two plates was an ancient ocean. The rocks formed from sediments piled up on the bed of the ocean were squeezed up into the Himalayas, which form the world's highest mountain range.

Above: Plates move past each other like two blocks of wood being pushed in opposite directions. But the movement is not smooth. The plate edges are jagged and the plates are usually locked together. But pressure finally breaks the locks. The plates then move suddenly in a violent jerk.

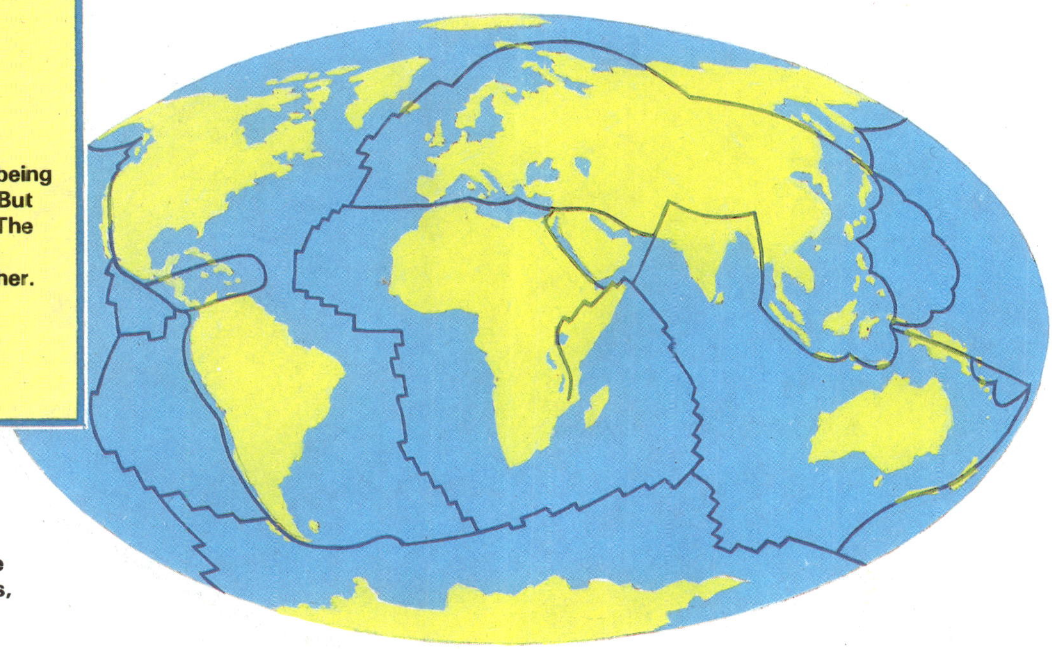

Right: The map shows the plates into which the Earth's surface is divided. The plates are all moving very slowly. The movements cause earthquakes, volcanic eruptions and the creation of mountain ranges.

Rocks of the Earth

Rocks consist of minerals and most rocks contain several minerals. There are three kinds of rocks: igneous rocks, metamorphic rocks and sedimentary rocks.

Igneous Rocks

The term igneous comes from a Latin word meaning 'fire', and all igneous rocks are formed from hot magma. When magma cools slowly underground, coarse-grained igneous rocks are formed. The grains (or mineral crystals) in the rock are visible with the naked eye. The commonest igneous rock formed in this way is granite.

Other igneous rocks form when magma cools quickly in the air or in water. Fast cooling prevents the formation of crystals and so these rocks are fine-grained. To see the minerals in fine-grained rocks, you must study them through a microscope. The commonest fine-grained igneous rock is basalt.

Metamorphic Rocks

When magma rises upwards, it heats the other rocks. Heat changes rocks, just as wet dough is turned into bread in a hot oven. Rocks are also changed by pressure and by chemical action caused by hot steam and liquids.

Rocks changed by heat, pressure or steam are called metamorphic rocks. The hard metamorphic rock slate (used for roofing) was formerly the soft rock shale or mudstone.

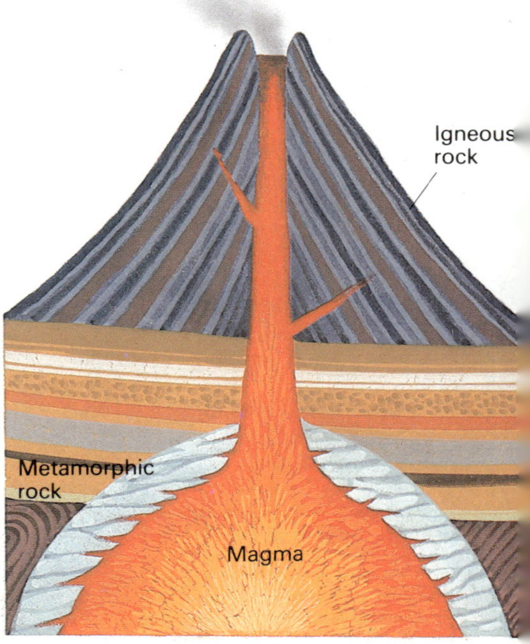

Below: The Grand Canyon is one of the most impressive sights in the world. This vast gorge in Arizona, USA, was cut out by the Colorado river, and in places it reaches a depth of more than 1.5 km. The successive layers of different coloured rocks give its steep walls a striped effect.

Marble is a metamorphic rock formed from limestone. Other metamorphic rocks include gneiss, hornfels and quartzite.

Sedimentary Rocks

Igneous and metamorphic rocks make up 95 per cent of the rocks in the top 16 km of the Earth's crust. But sedimentary rocks cover 75 per cent of the Earth's land surface.

Many sedimentary rocks consist of worn fragments of other rocks. These fragments are piled up, usually in water, and pressed into layers. The loose grains are later cemented together by minerals deposited from seeping water. Such rocks include sandstone and shale. Some sedimentary rocks are deposited from water. They include flint, rock salt and some kinds of limestone. Other limestones consist largely of the remains of dead sea creatures. Coal is another sedimentary rock. It consists of the remains of ancient plants.

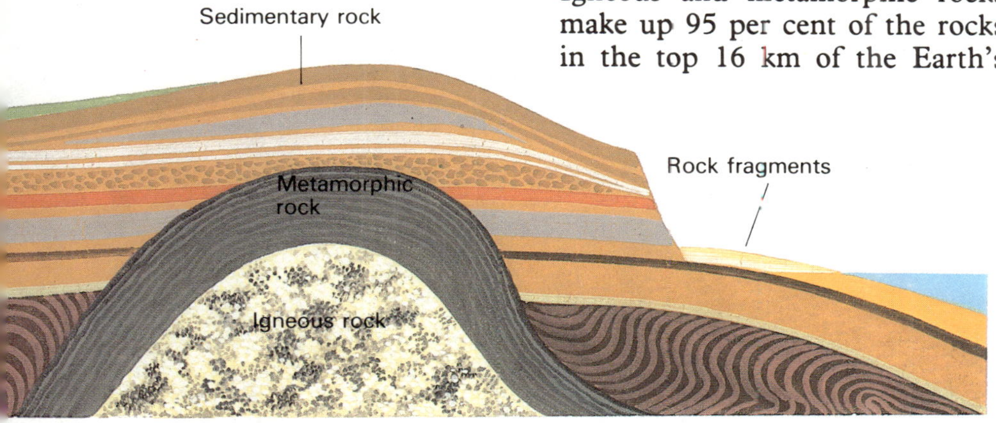

Above: The diagram shows the main kinds of rock. Igneous rocks are formed when molten magma is pushed upwards through the Earth's crust and cools and hardens. Some magma reaches the surface and some cools underground. Metamorphic rocks are rocks that have been changed by great heat or by pressure. The third type is called sedimentary rock. Many sedimentary rocks are formed from fragments of sand, mud or the remains of dead sea creatures which pile up in water.

Right: Mountaineers have climbed most of the world's highest peaks, including Mount Everest. Everest is in the Himalayas, on the border between Nepal and China.

Mountains

The four main kinds of mountains are fold mountains, block mountains and volcanic and dome mountains.

Fold Mountains

Folds are bends in layers of rock caused by sideways movements in the Earth's crust. Upfolds are called anticlines and downfolds are called synclines.

Fold mountains rise when two plates in the Earth's crust push against each other. Flat layers of rock between the plates are then buckled upwards into huge loops. For example, the Himalayas are fold mountains caused by a collision between a plate bearing India and another plate bearing the rest of Asia (see pages 10-11). The Alps started to rise when, about 26 million years ago, the African plate pushed a small plate bearing Italy against the underside of Europe.

Block Mountains

When plates move, they crack nearby rocks. Long cracks are called faults. Plate movements cause faults to open up and push the cracked rocks up and down along the faults. Large blocks of land squeezed upwards along faults are called horsts or block mountains.

Volcanic and Dome Mountains

Volcanic mountains are made up of erupted magma. Sometimes magma rises upwards but does not reach the surface. It pushes the overlying rocks up into domes. When the overlying rocks are worn away, the hardened magma is exposed as a dome mountain.

Fold mountains are formed by lateral (sideways) pressure. Flat layers of rock are arched up into folds. Fold mountain ranges include the Himalayas in Asia, the Alps in Europe, the Rockies in North America and the Andes in South America.

Fast-flowing rivers in mountainous regions wear out deep, V-shaped valleys.

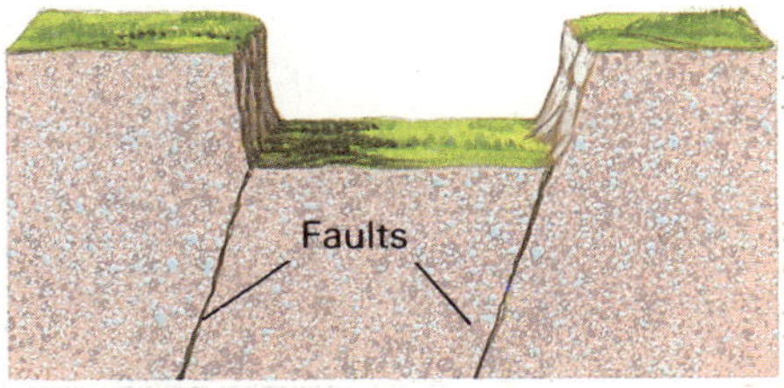

Rift valleys form when blocks of land sink downwards between two sets of faults.

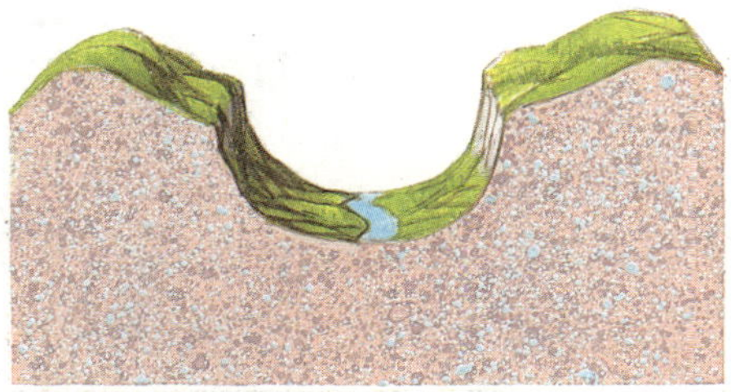

Steep-sided U-shaped valleys are worn out by glaciers (tongues of ice) in mountain regions.

Valleys and Slopes

Even as mountains are pushed upwards, so the forces of erosion start to wear them down. Weathering breaks up rocks. Rivers and glaciers carry worn material away. In doing so, they wear out deep valleys. Rift valleys are not eroded. They are formed when blocks of land slip down between faults.

Steep slopes are the main feature of mountain areas. Rocks on steep slopes are unstable. They may be dislodged by earthquakes to cause landslides, earth flows (movements of fine soil and clay), mud flows (made of dust and sand or volcanic ash mixed with water), and avalanches (falls of ice, snow and rock).

Landslides are movements of soil and rock down a cliff or mountainside. Landslides can do much damage and cause loss of life.

KINDS OF MOUNTAINS

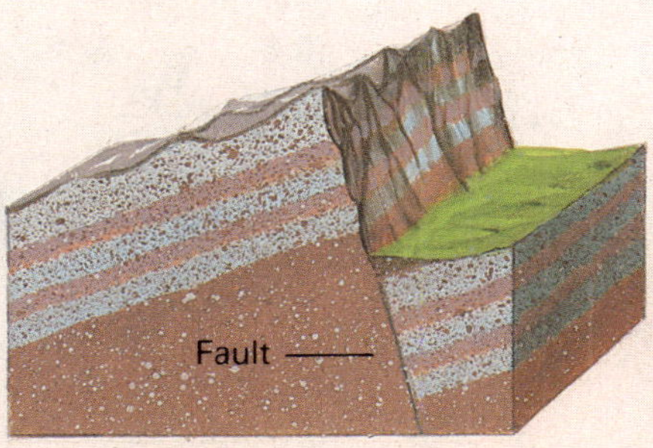

Block mountains are formed when a large block of land is pushed upwards along a fault (crack) or between two faults in the Earth's crust. The Sierra Nevada range in California in the south-western United States is an example of a block mountain.

Some volcanic mountains consist of volcanic ash and other fragments of magma which have been exploded into the air. Others are huge piles of hardened lava. Most volcanoes contain layers of ash alternating with layers of lava.

LANDSLIDES AND AVALANCHES

Some of the most destructive landslides and avalanches are caused by earthquakes.

For example, an earthquake in 1840 caused a landslide in the Himalayas. Rocks crashed down a gorge into the Indus River. The rocks dammed the river and a 64-km long lake formed behind the rocks. When the dam burst, a flood destroyed everything in its path for hundreds of kilometres downstream.

A landslide in Italy in 1963 sent many rocks crashing into a man-made lake. Water surged over the dam, wiping out the resort of Longarone.

In 1970, an avalanche in Peru killed 18,000 people.

Volcanoes

Volcanoes are vents (holes) in the ground where magma reaches the Earth's surface. The magma may appear in flows of molten lava or as fragments, including volcanic ash and sizeable volcanic bombs. Mountains built of magma are also called volcanoes.

There are more than 500 active volcanoes. Active volcanoes have erupted in historic times. Between eruptions, they are dormant (sleeping). Volcanoes that are unlikely to erupt again are extinct.

Where Volcanoes Occur

Most volcanoes lie near the edges of the moving plates in the Earth's crust (see pages 10-11). Some are on the ocean ridges. Others are near places where one plate is descending beneath another. The descending plate is melted to produce magma. A few volcanoes, like those in Hawaii, lie far from plate edges. They are probably above hot spots in the Earth's mantle.

Right: This diagram of a volcano shows that magma rises from an underground chamber (1) to the crater (2) during eruptions. Ash is sometimes exploded into the air while lava (3) flows from the crater. The ash and lava pile up to form a volcanic mountain. Sheets of magma are forced into nearby rocks. Some called dykes (4) cut across existing layers, while sills (5) run between existing layers. Some magma may be forced through secondary vents (6) in the side of the mountain. Runny lava may rise through long faults (7) and spread out over the land. Extinct volcanoes (8) have not erupted in historic times. Magma heats water in the rocks. Some water appears in hot springs and geysers (9), which are high jets of hot water and steam.

Volcanoes formed from ash and cinder are steep-sided. Cones like these often build up inside craters between major eruptions.

Thick, pasty lava flows only a short distance before it hardens. It also forms volcanic mountains with steep slopes.

Runny lava flows great distances. As a result, it forms flattened volcanoes, like upturned saucers, as in Hawaii.

Kinds of Volcanoes

Some volcanoes erupt in huge explosions. These volcanoes contain pasty magma. Lots of gases and steam are trapped in the magma. The vent of the volcano is usually blocked by a hard plug of magma. Below, the magma is pushing upwards until the pressure becomes so great that the plug is removed. Hot gases and steam then surge from the vent, often followed by a dark cloud of hot ash which races down the mountainside. Huge columns of ash are hurled into the air.

Quiet volcanoes, by contrast, usually contain runny magma, from which gases and steam can easily escape. They do not erupt in great explosions. Instead, they emit long streams of fluid lava. However, most volcanoes are intermediate in type. They sometimes erupt explosively and sometimes quietly.

Predicting Eruptions

Scientists keep watch on many active volcanoes. They look out for small earthquakes, swellings in the sides of the mountains and increases in temperatures and pressure. When they think an eruption is likely, they warn people and ask them to leave the area.

GREAT VOLCANIC ERUPTIONS

GREATEST VOLCANIC EXPLOSION: A volcano on the Greek island of Thera (Santorini) exploded in about 1470 BC with the power of about 130 times the greatest H-bomb detonation.
GREATEST MODERN EXPLOSION: People 4700 km away heard the volcanic explosion on the Indonesian island of Krakatoa in 1883. But this explosion was probably only about one-fifth as powerful as that at Thera.
GREATEST ERUPTION: Tambora, a volcano on the Indonesian island of Sumbawa, erupted in 1815. It was the greatest in terms of the amount of rock removed. The total amount of rock exploded away was probably two and a half to three times as much as at Thera.

Earthquakes

The Trembling Earth

Earthquakes can occur anywhere. They may be caused by landslides or by volcanic eruptions. But most are caused by movements along faults in rocks which shake the land. Most do little or no damage. But a few earthquakes cause great destruction.

The place inside the Earth where an earthquake occurs is called the focus. The most destructive earthquakes have a focus that is within about 60 km of the surface. Earth movements at much deeper levels have less effect at the surface. The point on the surface above the focus is called the epicentre. The epicentres of many earthquakes are in the oceans. The tremors may set off fast moving waves called tsunamis. Tsunamis can cause great damage far away from the epicentre.

Below: The map shows that most earthquakes occur in clearly defined zones. Earthquakes can occur anywhere, but most of them, including the most intense, are concentrated around the edges of the moving plates into which the Earth's crust is divided.

Bottom: During severe earthquakes, like the one that hit Anchorage and other towns in Alaska in 1964, large cracks may open up in the shaking ground. Buildings collapse and landslides often cause great damage. Other hazards include fires, which often do even more damage than the earthquake, and tsunamis (high waves) that strike coastal areas, sweeping ships inland.

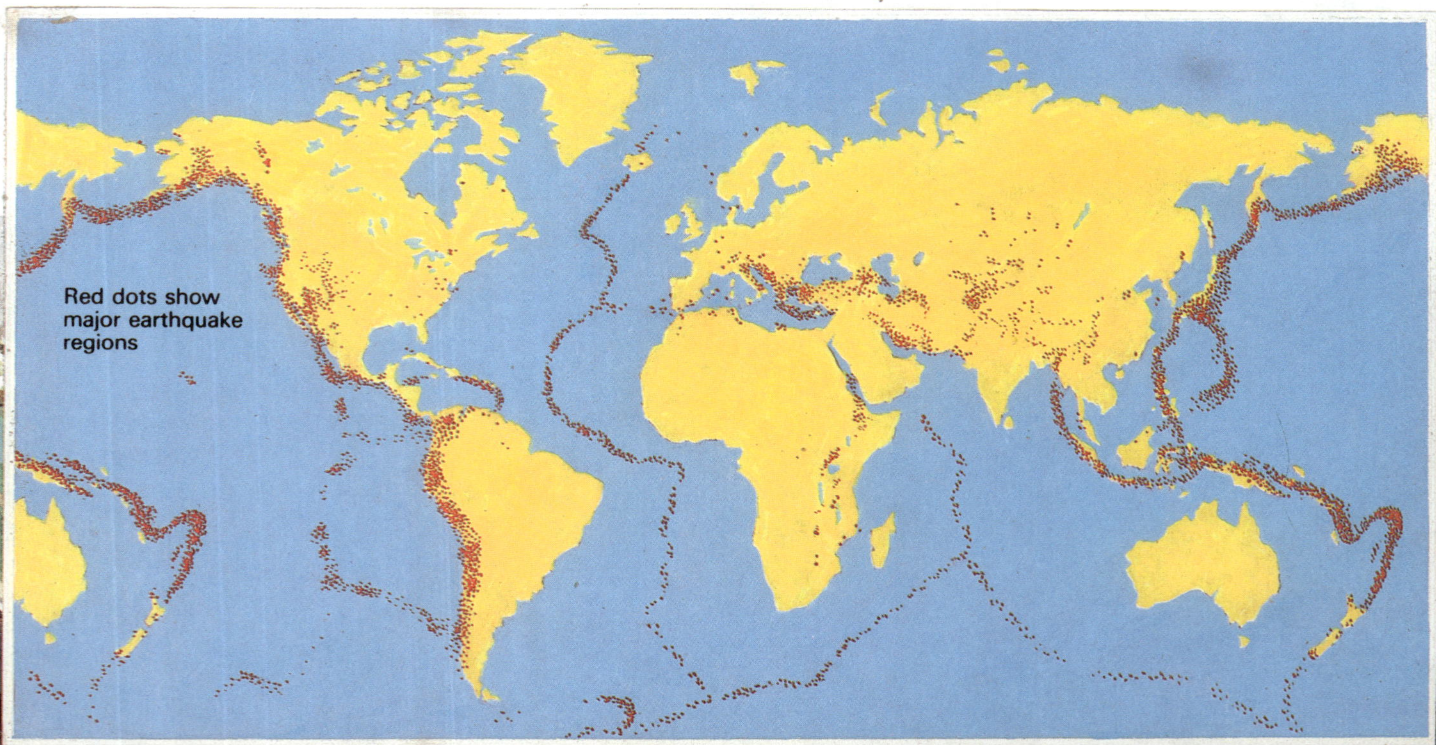

Where Earthquakes Occur

The chief earthquake zones follow the edges of the plates in the Earth's crust, namely the ocean ridges, zones where one plate is descending beneath another, and transform faults. Earthquakes occur when plates move in sudden jerks. The San Andreas (transform) fault runs through California, in the south-western USA. A movement along this fault in 1906 shook the city of San Francisco. Fires destroyed much property. Since 1906, scientists have found ways of building houses that will not collapse during 'quakes.

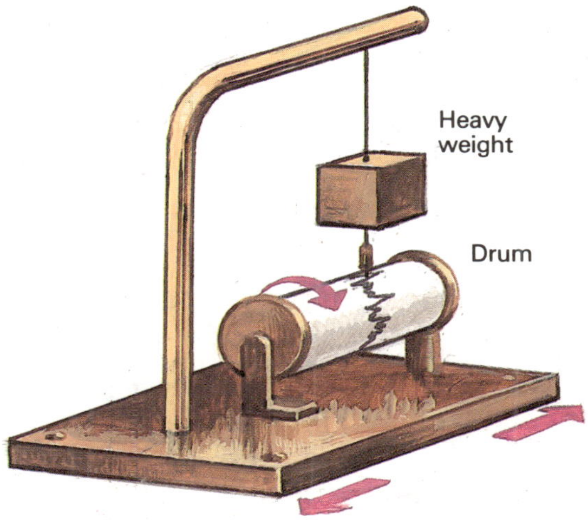

Above: Seismographs are sensitive instruments used to record earthquakes. When an earthquake occurs, the heavy weight suspended from the frame stays almost still while the support shakes. The vibrations are recorded on a piece of paper wrapped around a slowly revolving drum.

Earthquake Prediction

Scientists want to find ways of predicting earthquakes. They have discovered that rocks may be deformed as pressure builds up before a 'quake. Other changes in rocks and even unusual behaviour by animals, which seem to sense danger, are also being studied. But earthquake forecasting is still a young science.

The Work of Rivers

Running water is a major force in shaping the land. In itself, water has little power to erode (wear away) rock. But rivers push loose boulders, stones and sand along their courses. As they do so, the loose material scrapes the river bed and loosens other rocks. In this way, rivers can wear out deep valleys. River water also dissolves some rocks. Of all the material carried by rivers, about 30 per cent is dissolved rock and 70 per cent is solid material. Most rivers can be divided into three distinctive stages. They are called youth, maturity and old age.

Above: Youthful rivers rise in glaciers, lakes or springs. They flow swiftly downhill and wear out deep V-shaped valleys. Erosion occurs when the river is in flood.

Youthful Rivers

Rivers originate in several ways. Some flow from melting glaciers. Some drain out of lakes. Others start in springs where water bubbles to the surface.

In mountain areas, youthful rivers flow rapidly straight down steep slopes. After rains or when snow melts in spring, they become raging torrents. They then wear away their beds and carve out deep, V-shaped valleys.

Above: In middle age, rivers develop meanders (bends) and so lateral (sideways) erosion becomes more important than downward erosion. As a result, the valleys become broader and broader.

Right: The diagram shows features of a river in old age. On straight stretches, the channel is symmetrical (1). On bends, the outer bend is undercut, but sediment is dumped on the inner bend (2). In old age, when a river floods, particles are dumped on the river banks to form mounds called levees (3). Other features are oxbow lakes (abandoned meanders) and deltas where the river divides into channels.

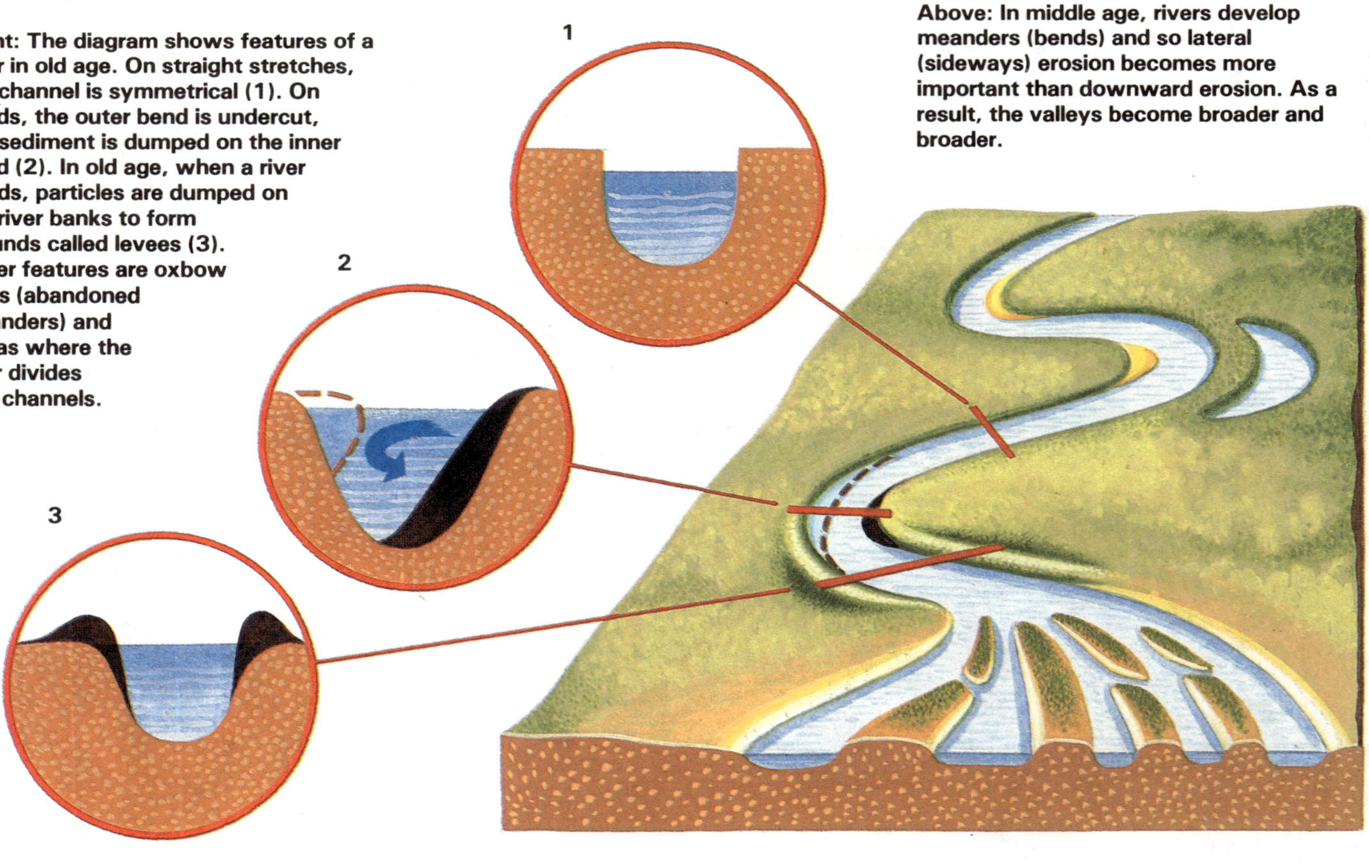

Left: In dry areas, fast-flowing rivers carve out deep gorges, as in the Big Bend part of the Rio Grande's course in Texas, USA.

Below: A section through a waterfall showing how the water undercuts the base of the rock face.

Mature Rivers

When rivers emerge from mountains, they slow down as they flow over less steep slopes. They develop large, sweeping bends, called meanders. Mature rivers do not deepen their valleys like youthful rivers. But the strong currents constantly widen the valleys.

Old Age Rivers

In old age, rivers flow slowly across nearly flat plains. There is little erosion, although the rivers carry huge amounts of fine sediment. When the rivers overflow, the sediment is spread over the land. Large particles are dropped on the river banks, where they pile up to form mounds called levees. Fine particles are swept long distances from the river.

In old age, rivers sometimes change course. They cut through the necks of bends and so straighten their courses. The bends then become 'abandoned meanders', or oxbow lakes, which later dry up. Some rivers dump much of their load of sediment at their mouths in areas called deltas. But in places where tidal currents are strong, the sediment is swept out to sea.

WATERFALLS

Many waterfalls, including Niagara Falls in North America, occur where rivers flow over hard rocks that resist erosion. The diagram, above, shows a waterfall of this kind. The softer rocks below are undercut so that, occasionally, parts of the overlying rock break off and crash down. Such falls gradually retreat upstream. On average, Niagara Falls is retreating by about 0.9 metres a year.

Other falls occur along steep escarpments that separate highlands from lowlands. Others occur in glaciated regions, where rivers plunge into deep U-shaped valleys.

The world's highest waterfall is Angel Falls, Venezuela. It is 979 metres high.

Shaping the Land

Right: Limestone caves are worn out by rainwater. Limestone consists mostly of calcium carbonate. This substance reacts chemically with rainwater, which eats away the rock along the horizontal and vertical cracks in the rock. Water seeping through the caves is highly charged with calcium carbonate.
Water dripping from the roof of a cave is often agitated and evaporated by air currents. Thin films of the mineral calcite are then deposited from the water. Layer upon layer of such deposits build downwards to form the icicle-like stalactites. Water splashing onto the floor of a cave also deposits calcite. These build upwards into stalagmites.

Although it is difficult to see, the land in your home area is slowly changing. American scientists have worked out that about 0.3 metres of land is removed from the eastern USA every 9000 years. This may not seem much. But if you remember that we measure Earth history in millions of years, you will realize that mountains can be worn down to plains. The main forces that shape the land are weathering, winds, rivers, ice and, along coasts, sea waves.

Weathering occurs in several ways. For example, rain is important, because some minerals, such as rock salt, dissolve in water. Some rocks, such as limestones, do not dissolve in pure water. But limestone dissolves in water which contains carbon dioxide dissolved from the air or soil. The dissolved gas changes the water into a weak acid. This acid wears out limestone caves.

Rainwater also affects the hard rock granite. This is because water combines with some kinds of feldspar and turns them into clay. The quartz and mica in granite are not affected. Grains of these minerals are washed away by rain and rivers. The quartz grains often form sandy beaches along coasts.

Above: Plants contribute to the break-up of rocks. Here, a seedling has taken root in a crack in a boulder. As the tree grows, the roots exert great pressure, pushing the boulder apart.

Weathering in Mountains and Deserts

In mountain areas, water seeps into cracks in rocks during the day. At night, temperatures often fall below zero and the water freezes. Ice occupies nine per cent more space than the same amount of water and so, when water freezes, it expands and the ice pushes against the sides of cracks. When this happens night after night, the cracks are widened and the rocks are finally split apart. This is called frost action. The shattered rocks tumble downhill. They often pile up in heaps called talus or scree.

In deserts, rocks are heated by the Sun by day. In the evening, temperatures fall quickly, often to below freezing point. The fast cooling of the rocks cracks the surfaces, making sounds like pistol shots. Layers of rock then peel away.

DESERT LANDSCAPES

There are three main kinds of desert landscapes: sandy deserts called *erg*; stony deserts called *reg*; and bare rocky deserts called *hammada*.

Deserts have little rain, but the main land features in most deserts were carved out by running water at a time when the climate was very different from that of today. Even now, a rare thunderstorm can drown areas which have been dry for years. *Wadis* (dry valleys) fill up with rushing torrents that sweep huge amounts of sand and rock away.

But wind-blown sand is the main natural form of erosion in deserts today. It can strip the paint off cars and undercut telegraph poles and boulders. It is responsible for mushroom-shaped boulders with a large top resting on a narrow stem. Wind-blown sand also grinds out deep hollows in rocky surfaces.

In sandy deserts, the wind blows the sand into dunes. *Barchans* are crescent-shaped dunes, while *seif dunes* are long sand ridges.

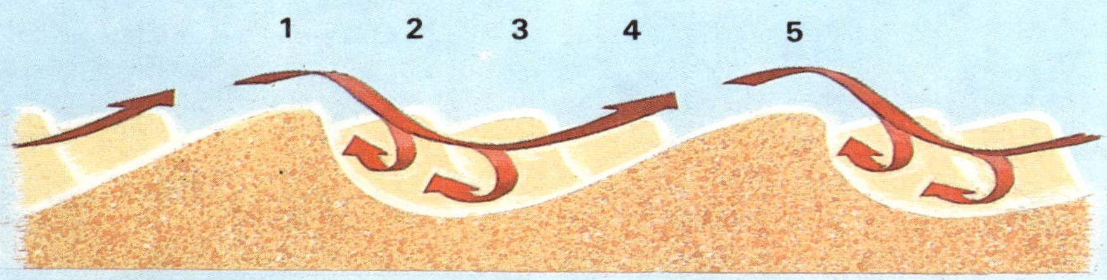

Sand covers about one-fifth of the world's deserts. Winds blow the grains of sand around, piling them up into hills called dunes. Dunes move in the direction of the prevailing (usual) wind. Grains of sand are blown up the gentle windward slopes and then topple down the steep slip faces. In this way, the dune slowly advances from position 1 to 2, 3, 4, 5 and so on.

Plants and Animals

As shown in the picture on the facing page, the roots of trees and shrubs can split rocks apart and so they also contribute to weathering. But plants also protect the land, especially when grass roots bind loose soil particles together.

Worms, which eat vast amounts of soil, and burrowing animals, such as rodents and termites, also play their part, because churned up soil is easily removed by rain and wind.

Right: Many desert features were carved by water at times in the past when the desert had a moist climate. Today, wind-blown sand eats away rocks along lines of weakness and polishes rocks, such as this natural arch.

The Sea in Motion

The oceans cover about 71 per cent of the Earth's surface. Ocean water is always moving, even in the deepest trenches. We know this because fishes live there. If the water was still, the oxygen dissolved in the water would have been used up long ago.

Above: When a wave passes through water, the particles of water rotate in a circular motion, but they are not moved sideways. The wave length is the distance between the crests of two successive waves. Along coasts, there is not enough water to complete the wave and so the wave breaks.

Winds and Waves
Waves appear to move seawater. In fact, they make water particles rotate, but do not move them forwards. Most waves are caused by winds. Tsunamis are waves generated by earthquakes. These low but fast-moving waves often pass unnoticed in the open sea. But near land, they build up to great heights. A tsunami off Japan reached a height of 85 metres.

High Tide, Low Tide
Tides are caused by the gravitational pull of the Moon and, to a lesser extent, of the Sun. They occur twice every 24 hours and 50 minutes. This is the time taken by the Moon to complete one orbit of the Earth.

Ships caught at sea during a bad storm run the risk of capsizing. The highest waves in the open sea are caused by strong winds. The highest recorded wave measured 34 metres between the trough and the crest.

Rivers in the Sea

Sailors are interested in ocean currents, because they affect navigation. These currents, which are caused mainly by prevailing winds, only affect the top 350 metres. Other currents lower down often move in an opposite direction to those on the surface. Many deep-sea currents are caused by variations in the density of the water. These result from differences in salinity (saltness) and temperature. Salty, cold water is denser (heavier) than less salty, warm water.

The circulation of ocean water by currents has an important effect on climate. Warm currents convey heat to cool temperate and polar regions. Cold currents also modify the climate of tropical regions.

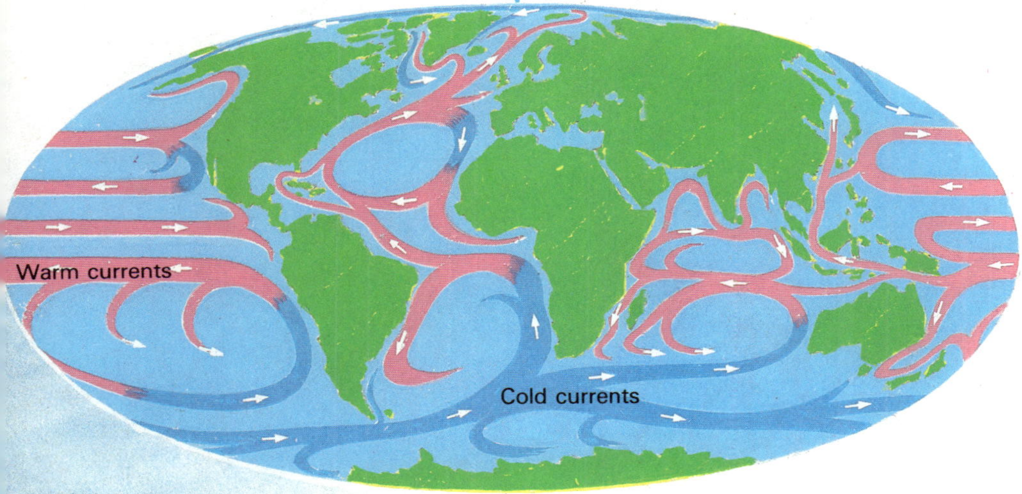

OCEAN CURRENTS

Ocean currents ensure that seawater is always on the move. The currents on the map (left) are caused mainly by winds. Ocean currents flow at 1-5 knots and so are important in navigation. Slower currents are called drifts. The slow northern extension of the fast Gulf Stream is the North Atlantic Drift.

Other currents flow at lower levels. For example, warm currents flow towards the polar regions. There, denser (heavier) cold polar water sinks beneath the warm water and flows towards the equator.

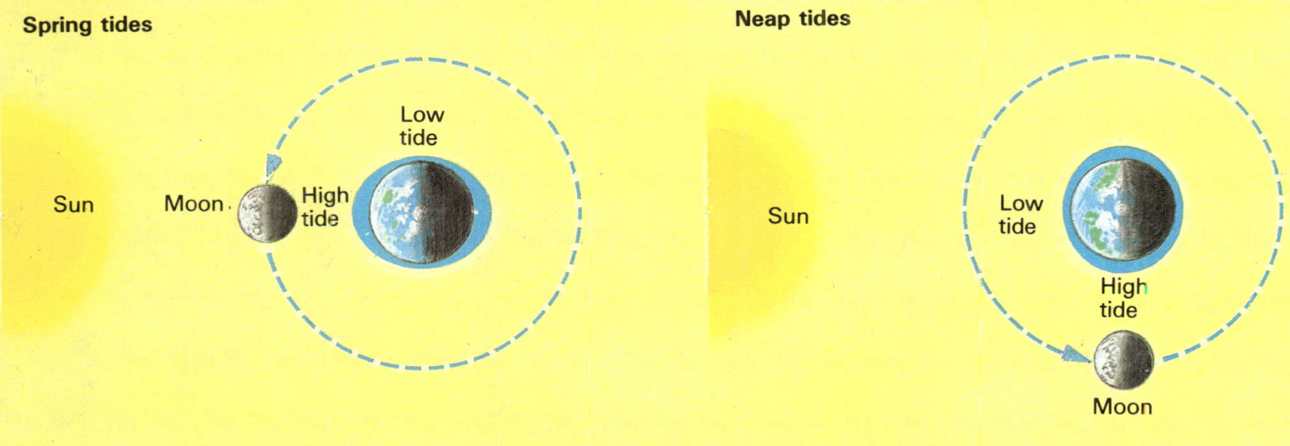

Tides are caused by the gravitational pull of the Moon and the Sun on the waters of the oceans. The highest tides are called spring tides. They occur when the Sun, Moon and Earth are in a straight line (above). The Moon's and the Sun's gravity are then combined.

The lowest tides are called neap tides. They occur when the Sun, Earth and Moon form a right angle (as shown above). The gravitational pull of the Moon is then opposed by the Sun's gravitational pull. Neap and spring tides each occur twice every month.

Mapping the Land

Maps show the world or parts of it on flat surfaces. Accurate maps are drawn to scale. At a scale of 1:50,000, 1 cm on the map equals 50,000 cm or 0.5 km on the ground.

Surveying the Land

The first job of land surveyors (people who measure the land) is to fix as accurately as possible the positions of a network of points, by measuring the angles and distances between them. Surveyors use telescopic instruments, theodolites, to measure angles. Measuring distances was once a slow process, using metal tapes. But surveyors can now use electronic instruments. When the positions of the points are known, their heights are measured. These fixed points, which are often marked on the ground by concrete pillars, form the skeleton of a map.

MAP SYMBOLS

CONTOURS are lines joining places with the same height. They are usually brown lines, but underwater contours are blue.
CULTURAL FEATURES are man-made things, such as towns, churches, historical sites, including battlefields (crossed swords), lighthouses, roads and railways. They usually appear in red or black.
HACHURES are fine lines that show land forms three-dimensionally.
LAYER TINTING is the use of colours and shades of colours to show the various levels of the land.
SPOT HEIGHTS are black dots or solid black triangles. A figure in metres or feet alongside the point shows the exact height.
VEGETATION FEATURES, such as forests and swamps, are usually depicted as green symbols.
WATER FEATURES, such as rivers, lakes and coasts, are shown in blue.

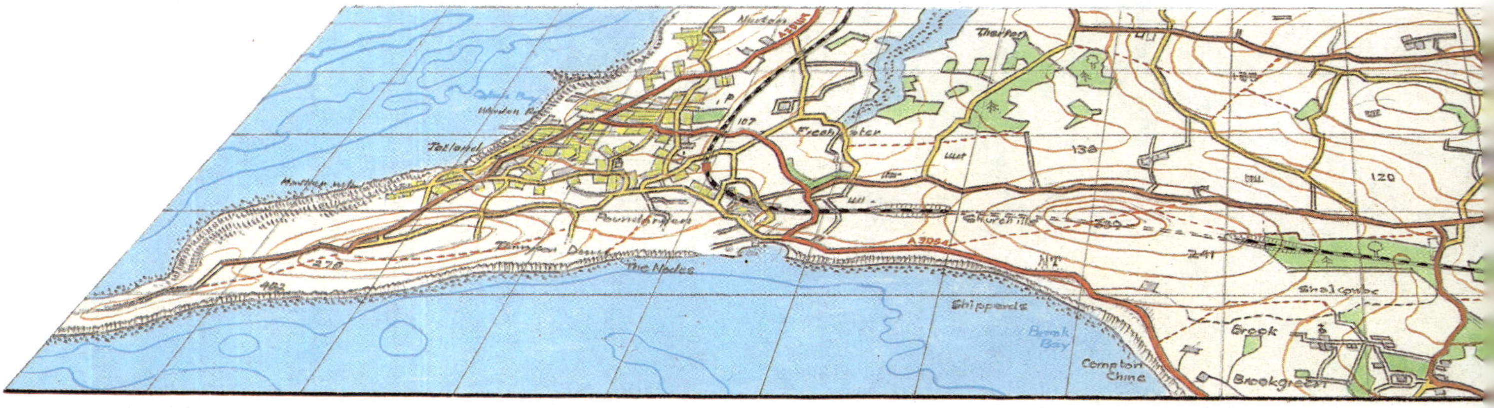

Detailed Mapping

When the network of points is fixed, surveyors must measure all the details of the land between them. This work was once done on the ground. But, today, mapping from air photographs has largely replaced ground mapping.

Aircraft take long strips of photographs of the land. Each photograph overlaps the next by 60 per cent. The fixed ground points are identified on the photographs. Because the distances between them are known, other distances can be measured on the photographs.

Heights can also be measured. This is because overlapping photographs viewed through a stereoscope appear as a three-dimensional model of the land.

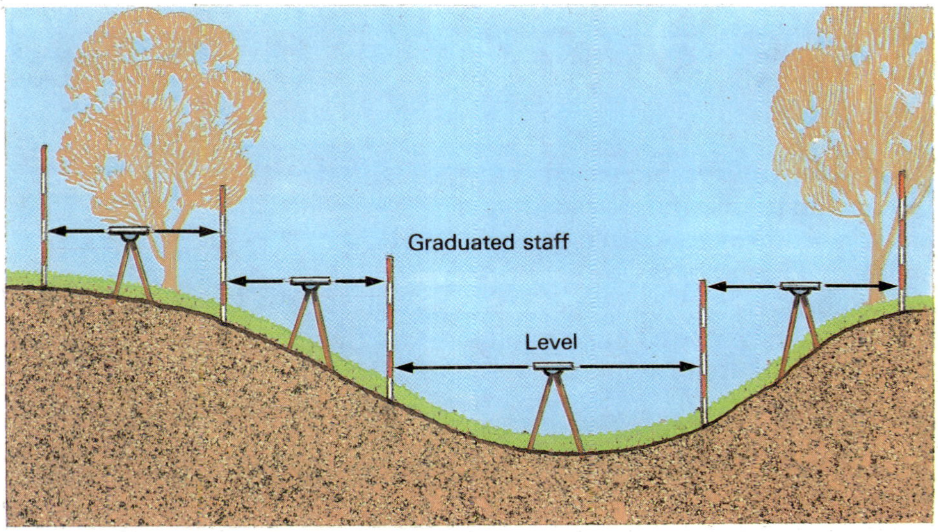

Above: To fix heights, surveyors use a telescopic instrument called a level, which is mounted on a tripod, and a graduated staff. The difference between the height of the level and a reading on the staff is the height difference between the two points.

Below: Topographic maps, or general reference maps, show the main features of the land over fairly small areas. They are drawn to scale so that any distance on the map represents a distance on the ground. In order to include as many details as possible, map-makers use symbols like those shown below. You will find a legend (key), containing all the symbols used on a map in the margins of most topographic maps.

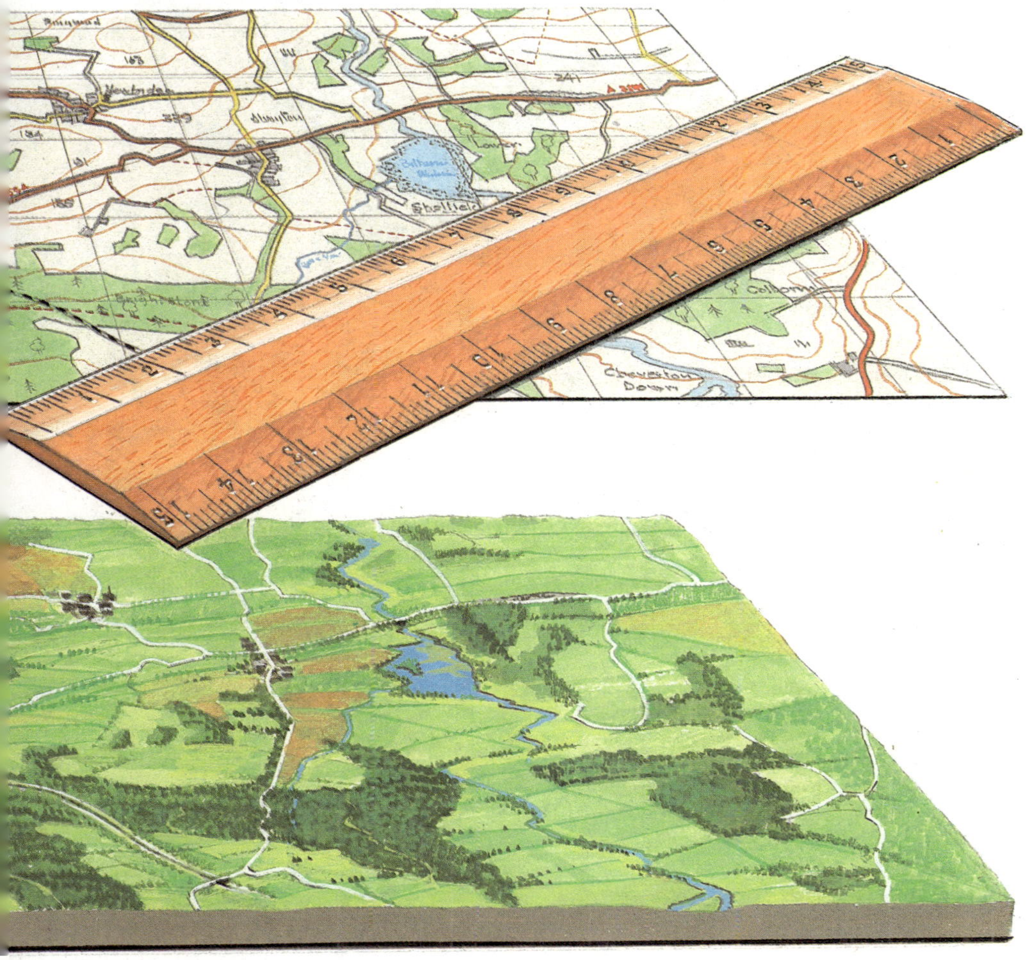

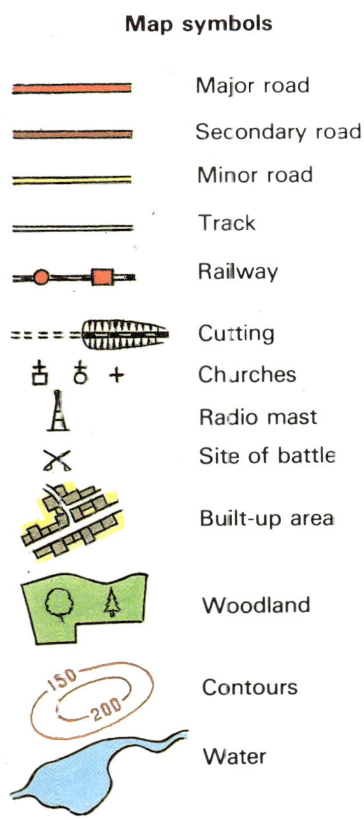

The World is Round

Geographers are interested in features on the Earth's surface and how the features are related to one another. The best way to present the information which geographers need is a map. The facts on a map would often fill a book.

Types of Maps

Apart from topographic, or general reference, maps, there are many special kinds of maps. For example, weather maps show the weather conditions over a large area, and population maps show where people are most concentrated. Special maps are now often produced by computers. They can be a great help to planners.

Some maps are large-scale, covering small areas. Maps with extremely large scales are called *plans*. But small-scale maps cover large areas. Such maps appear in atlases. Small-scale maps create problems for map-makers.

Curved Surfaces, Flat Maps

A major problem faced by map-makers is that the Earth is nearly a sphere. Its surface is curved, not flat. To understand the problem, think of another sphere, an orange.

If you peel an orange, keeping the peel in one piece, you are left with a hollow sphere. It is impossible to turn this sphere into a flat surface without breaking it and crushing the pieces. To deal with this problem, map-makers have devised various solutions — map projections.

Map Projections

Map projections are ways of *projecting* details on a curved surface onto a flat surface.

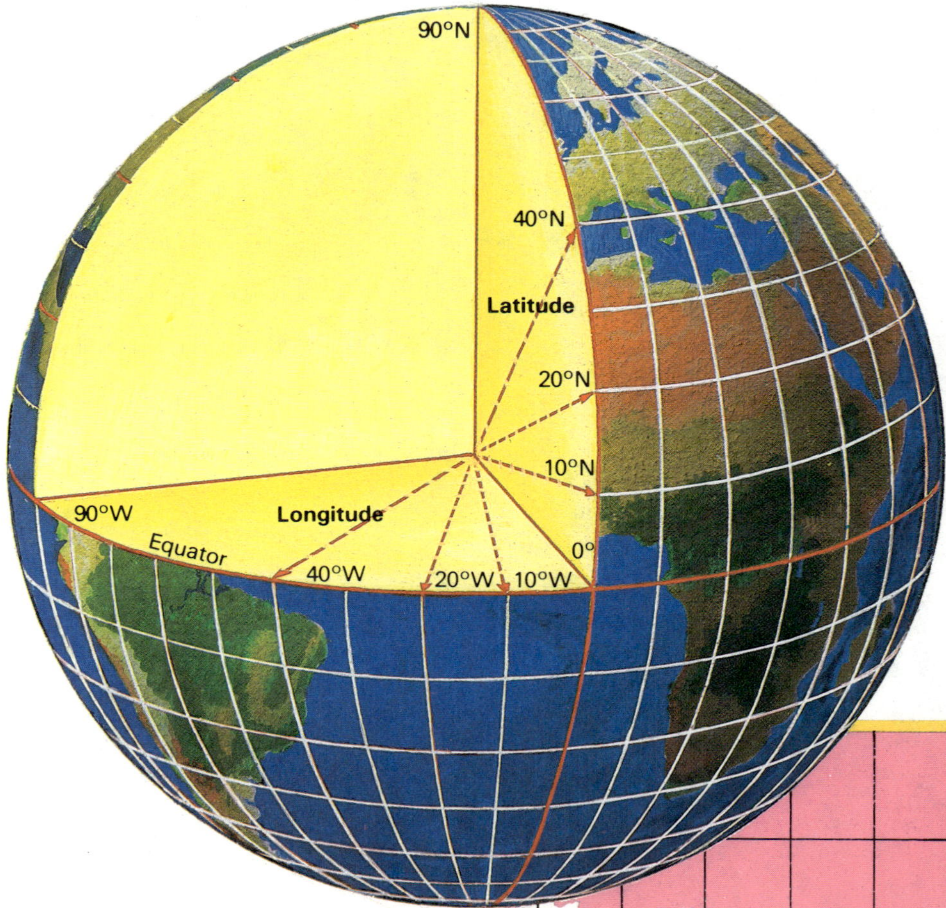

Above: The latitude of a place is the angle formed at the centre of the Earth between the equator (0 degrees latitude) and that place. Longitude is measured around the equator by the angle formed at the centre of the Earth between the prime meridian (0 degrees longitude) and the place. The prime meridian passes through Greenwich, in England. Lines of longitude are called meridians. And lines of latitude are called parallels.

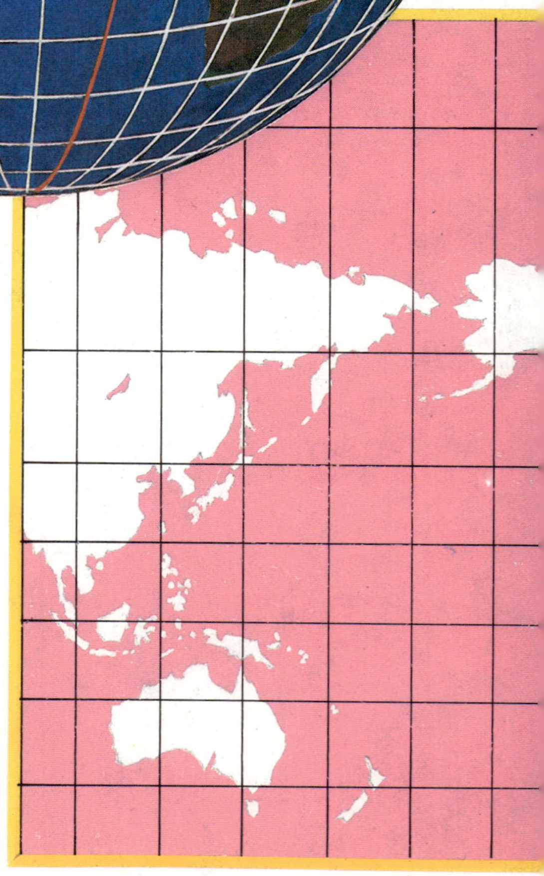

Right: Mercator's world map is a type of cylindrical projection (see diagram opposite). The poles, which are points, appear as lines as long as the equator. This distortion makes areas far from the equator, such as Greenland, look bigger than they really are.

Some projections are devised as though the Earth is a glass sphere with all the details and lines of latitude and longitude engraved on it. If you place a light at the center of the globe, the engraved lines are projected as shadows onto flat surfaces. A cylindrical projection of this type is shown below. But most projections are worked out by mathematics.

No one map can show shapes, areas, distances and directions correctly at the same time. Only a globe can do that. Some map projections preserve some features and some preserve others. Equal area maps, for instance, ensure that all countries are the right *size*. Conformal maps make sure that the *shape* of the countries is correct. The type of projection depends on the purpose of the map.

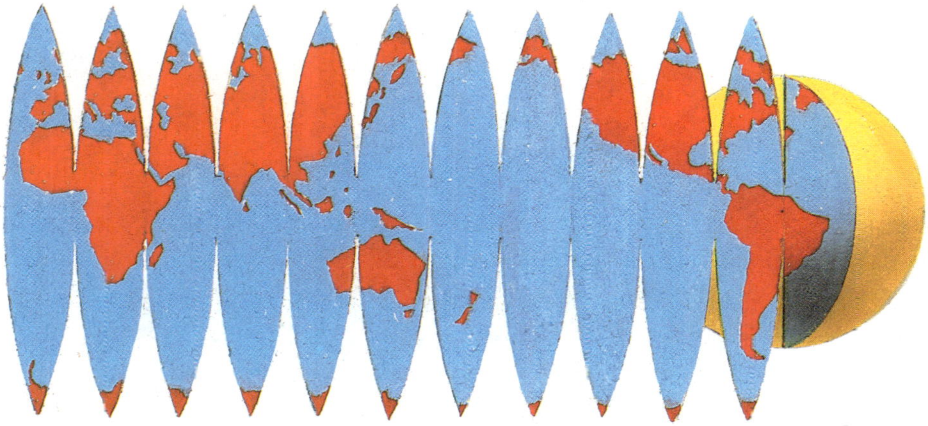

Above: The problem of showing a curved surface on a flat piece of paper is revealed when globes are made. The world map is first printed on a series of thin, lens-shaped pieces of paper, called gores. The gores are fitted together on the globe and pasted down. Some map projections are drawn in separate sections, resembling gores. Such projections are said to be interrupted. Maps based on interrupted projections are of little use, however, because they split up land masses.

Below: Cylindrical map projections are developed as though a light was placed at the center of an engraved glass globe. Around the globe is a cylinder of paper, touching the globe along the equator. The light casts shadows of the engraved meridians and parallels, together with the shapes of the continents, onto the paper. This creates a map. But you can see that the distances between lines of latitude increase towards the poles. On a true map, these distances should be the same.

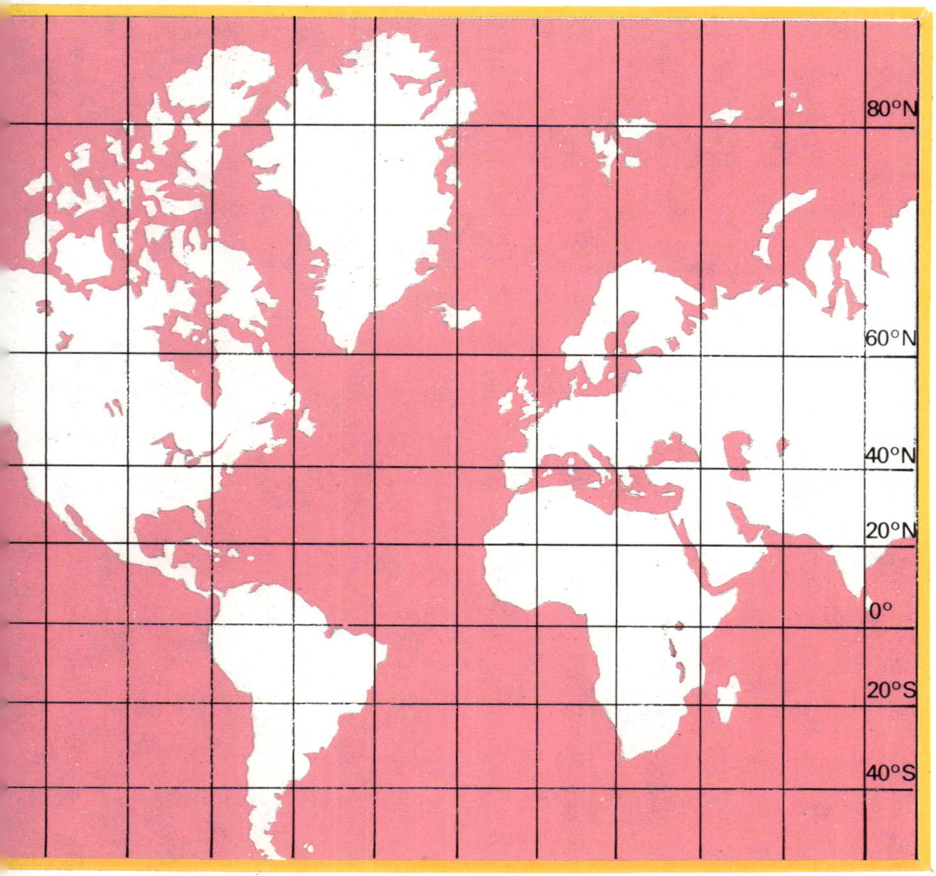

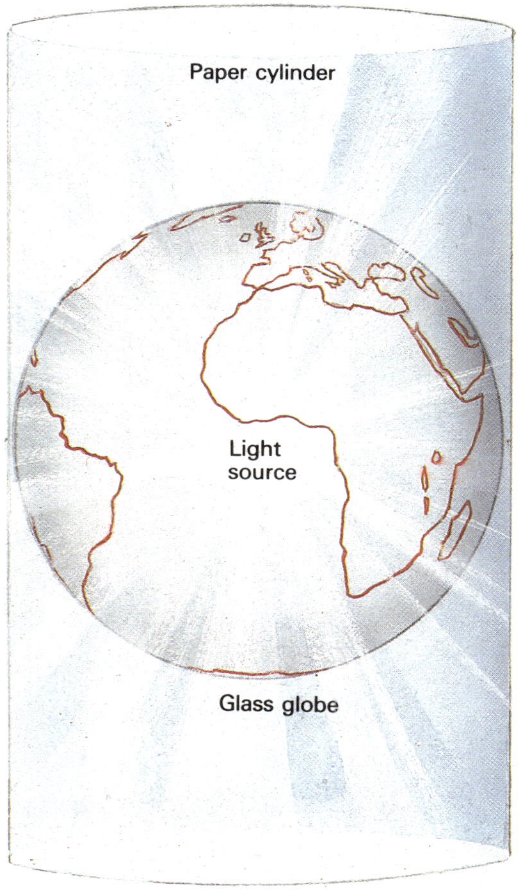

Cloud, Wind and Rain

Air is always moving because of the Sun's heat. At the equator, hot air rises. This creates a zone of low air pressure at the surface, called the *doldrums*. The rising air eventually cools and spreads out north and south. It finally sinks back to the Earth at around latitude 30° North and 30° South. These are the *horse latitudes*. Regions where air is sinking are high air pressure zones. From the horse latitudes, trade winds blow towards the equator and westerly winds blow towards the poles. From the poles — also high air pressure regions — come the polar easterlies. The trade winds, westerlies and polar easterlies are the prevailing (chief) winds of their various regions.

The Sun evaporates water from the oceans. Warm air can hold more water vapour than cold air. But when warm air rises and cools, it finally reaches *dew point*, when the air contains all the vapour it can at that temperature. More cooling makes water vapour *condense* (liquefy) into water droplets or ice crystals, which form clouds. In clouds, water droplets collide to become raindrops. The ice crystals also grow in size. They fall as snow or, in warm air, as raindrops.

Cirrus (a high cloud) is wispy and made of ice crystals.

Cirrocumulus (a high cloud) is thin with ripples or rounded masses.

Cirrostratus (a high cloud) may cause halos around the Sun or Moon.

Altocumulus (a medium cloud) consists of rounded masses.

Altostratus (a medium cloud) is a greyish sheet cloud.

Cumulus (a low cloud) is a white heap cloud.

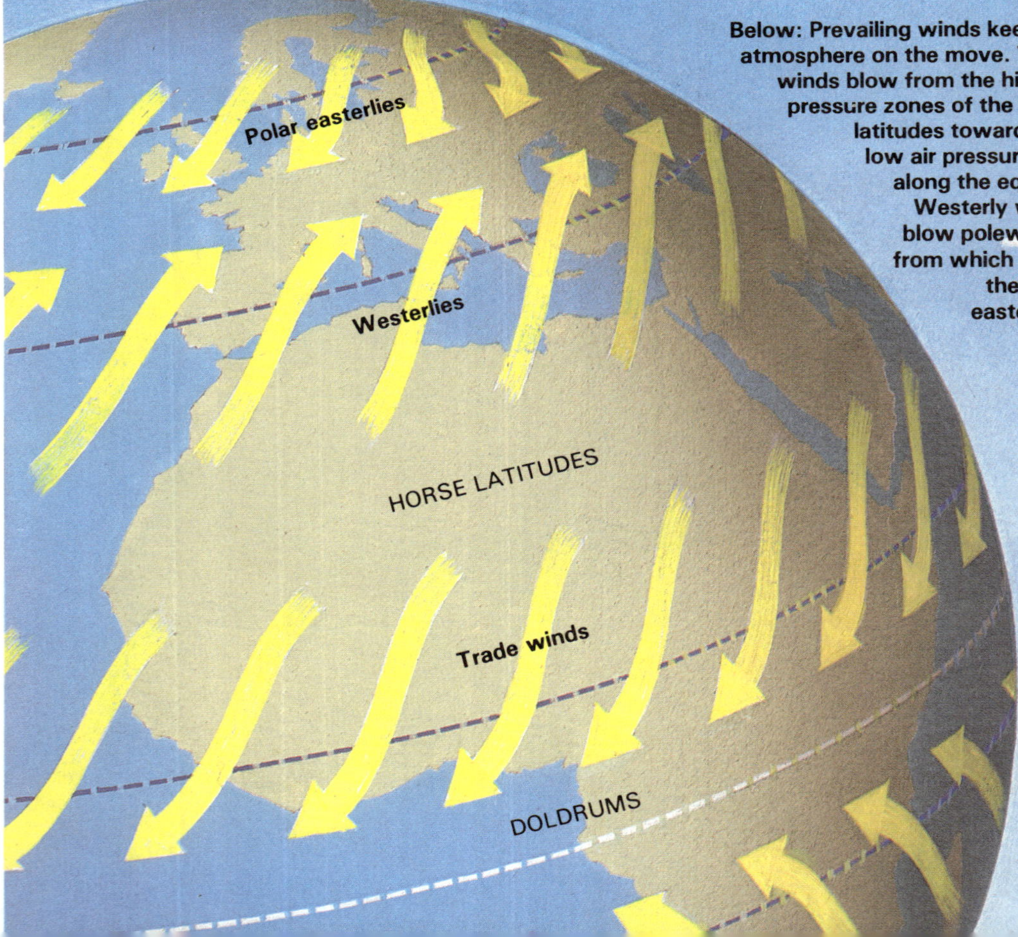

Below: Prevailing winds keep the atmosphere on the move. Trade winds blow from the high air pressure zones of the horse latitudes towards the low air pressure belt along the equator Westerly winds blow polewards, from which come the polar easterlies.

Cumulonimbus (thundercloud) may extend from 300 to 12,000 metres.

(1) Orographic rain occurs when winds blow over mountains. The rising air cools, clouds form and rain falls on the windward slopes. Beyond the mountain tops, the air descends and gets warmer, drying the land. This is a rain shadow region.

(2) Convectional rain occurs when the Sun heats the Earth's surface which, in turn, heats the air near the ground. The warm air rises in fast currents. Eventually, the rising air cools, clouds form and rain starts to fall.

(3) Cyclonic rain occurs in depressions (or cyclones) when warm air rises above blocks of cold air.

Stratus (a low cloud) is a grey layer cloud.

Climates of the World

The climate is the average, or usual, weather of a place. Climates vary between the poles and the equator.

Climatic Regions

There are six main climatic regions. *Polar climates* are regions where the average temperature in the warmest month is less than 10°C. This is the climate of the frozen wastes around the poles and also the tundra, where the snow melts in summer.

Cold (coniferous) *forest* climates occur in a zone that stretches across North America and Eurasia. The average temperature in the coldest month is less than -3°C. But in the warmest month, the average temperature is above 10°C.

Temperate climates have an average temperature in the coldest month of not less than -3°C, but not more than 18°C. This climate includes mixed forest, deciduous forest and Mediterranean regions.

In *dry climates*, the total average yearly rainfall is less than 250 mm. Deserts may be hot or cold.

Tropical rainy climates have average temperatures in every month that are higher than 18°C. Some places have rain throughout the year. Others have one or two marked dry seasons.

Mountain climates vary as one climbs upwards, because temperatures fall with height. Some mountains on the equator have tropical climates at the bottom and polar climates at their snow-capped tops.

Above: Dense rain forests flourish in tropical rainy climates, where high temperatures and abundant rainfall encourage plant growth. The thickest forests are in regions which have rain throughout the year. Less dense forests grow in monsoon regions which have a marked dry season.

Left: In hot deserts, the only places with water are oases. Many oases are springs or wells which get water from the rocks below. Palm trees grow around them and camels can get much-needed water.

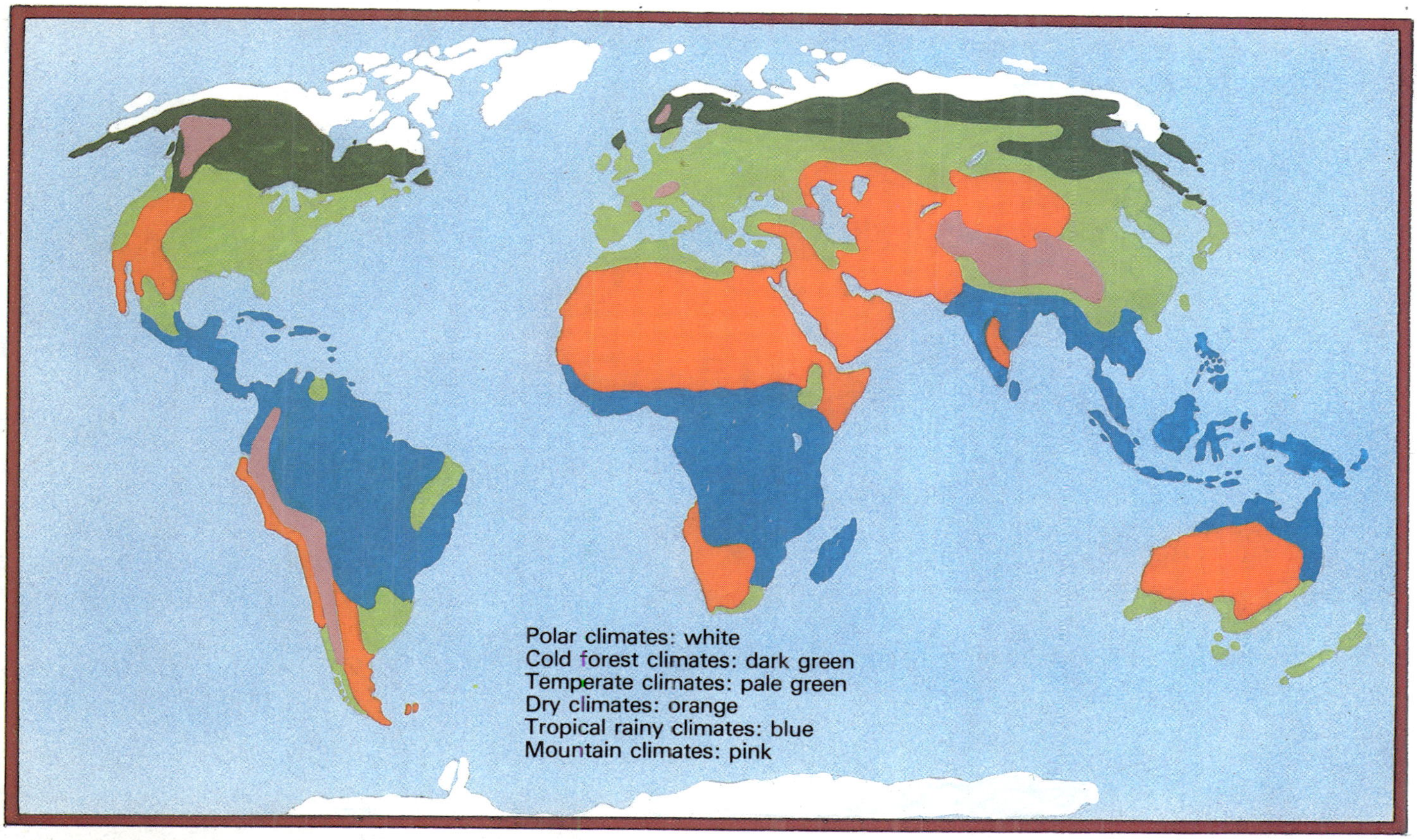

Above: Vast coniferous forests, called taiga, grow in the northern hemisphere in the cold region between the temperate lands to the south and the tree-line, the northernmost limit of tree growth. Birds such as this capercaillie are quite common, though compared with other forests there are few plant and animal species.

Above: The temperate regions of the world were once covered by deciduous trees, which shed their leaves in winter. But most of the trees have now been cut down and replaced by farmland.

Top: The map shows the major climatic regions of the world.

Above: Around the poles, ice and snow blanket the land all the year round. But in the northern hemisphere, between the lands of permanent ice and the tree-line, is a zone called the tundra. This zone comes alive during the short, warm summer when the snow melts. Animal migrants such as musk-oxen and reindeer graze on the tundra. And the arctic fox's white coat turns red during the short summer months.

Industry

Industry Around the World

In the last 200 years, the economies of many countries have changed, as farming and small-scale craft industries have become less important than mining and large-scale factory production. Such countries have been *industrialized*. The Industrial Revolution began in Britain in the late 18th century and Belgium, France, Germany and the USA soon followed. In the late 19th century, other countries, such as Canada, Japan, Russia and Sweden also began to industrialize.

The Pattern of Industry

The industrialized world now includes most of North America, Europe, the USSR, Japan, Australia and New Zealand. But most of Central and South America, Africa and Asia have not been industrialized, although some countries, such as Brazil and China, already have sizeable industries which are expected to expand rapidly in the near future. Many poor countries would like to industrialize, but they lack the money and skilled workers needed to found industries.

Light and Heavy Industry

Light industry produces a wide range of goods, which are generally smaller than those produced by heavy industry. For example, the many consumer products which we find in supermarkets, including clothes, foods and household goods, are produced by light industries. Light industries are now changing because of the introduction of computers and automation.

Heavy industry is associated with huge factories, which use bulky raw materials to produce heavy products. Examples include the iron and steel industry, the chemical industry and heavy engineering, such as shipbuilding. Heavy industries were once located on coal- or iron-fields, because this reduced the cost of transporting these heavy raw materials. But many industries which use oil have spread to other areas in recent years. This is because oil is easily transported through pipelines.

Some industries are neither light nor heavy. For example, car assembly and aerospace industries combine elements from both.

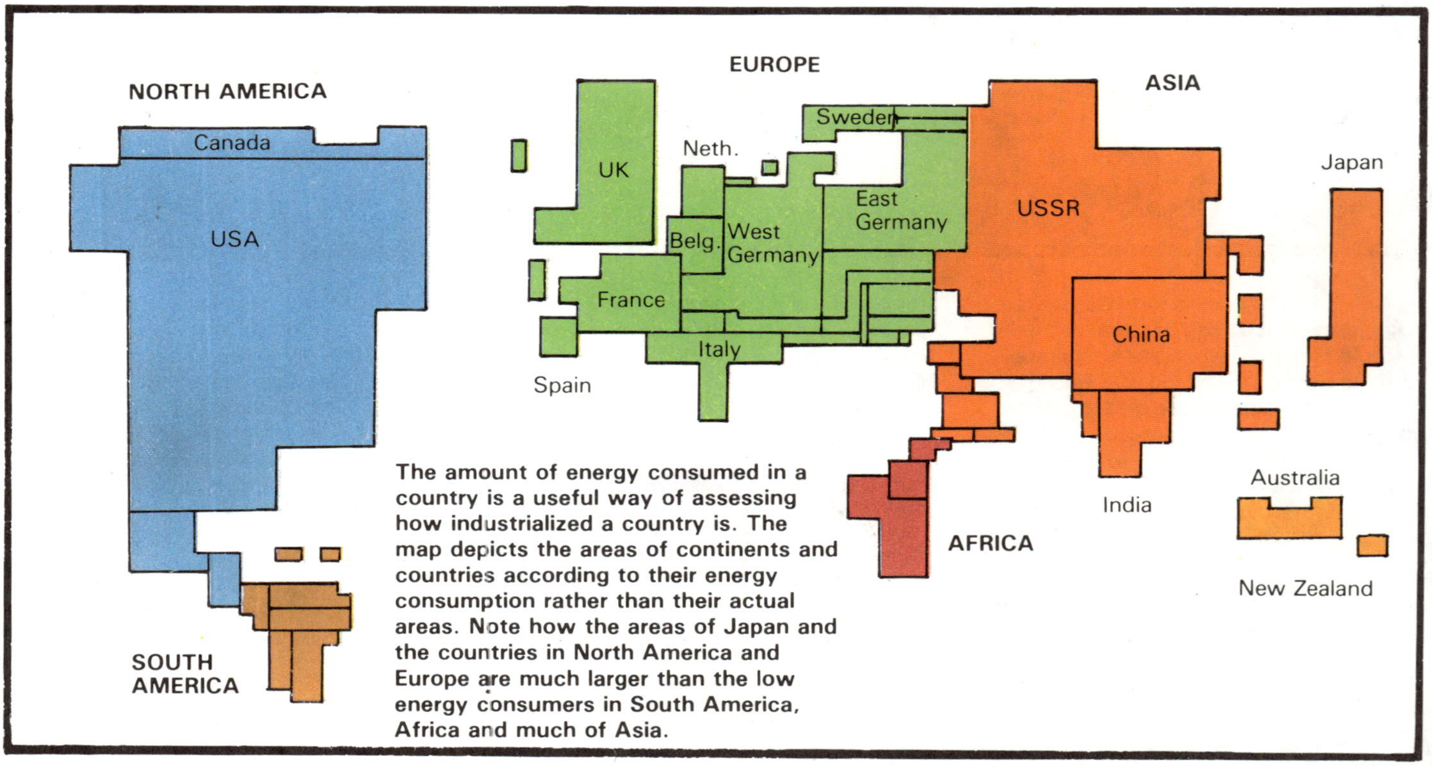

The amount of energy consumed in a country is a useful way of assessing how industrialized a country is. The map depicts the areas of continents and countries according to their energy consumption rather than their actual areas. Note how the areas of Japan and the countries in North America and Europe are much larger than the low energy consumers in South America, Africa and much of Asia.

Steel is the most important material used in shipbuilding, one of the world's leading heavy industries. In recent years, shipbuilders have made larger ships, including vast oil tankers, which can carry large amounts of bulk freight. Europe was once the main centre of shipbuilding. But by the early 1980s Japan led the world, producing 48% of the world's merchant vessels. At the end of the 1980s Japan was still the world's biggest producer of merchant ships, making 37% of the world's output. South Korea was in second place with 29%. Following these two countries were West Germany and Taiwan.

Farming Round the World

Some countries are densely populated, but have only a small area of flat farmland. They build terraces, like a series of steps, down hillsides. The walls around the terraces stop rainwater running downwards washing away the soil.

The world's chief farming nations are China, the USSR, the USA and India. But their farming industries differ greatly. In the USSR and the USA, farmers use modern machinery and yields are high. In China and India, much of the work is done by hand and yields are lower.

There are two main types of farming. Arable farming is the growing of crops. Pastoral farming is the production of meat and other animal products.

Tropical Farming

Many farmers in the tropics are poor, producing only enough food for their families. This is subsistence farming. Some farmers move every few years, whenever the fertility of their farms is exhausted. Nomadic pastoralists wander around with their animals. These simple forms of farming contrast with tropical plantation agriculture, which uses scientific methods to produce such cash crops as cocoa, coffee and tea.

THE INVENTION OF FARMING

Farming was invented about 10,000 years ago, when people learned how to plant seeds. The earliest known farms were in south-western Asia, but farming began soon afterwards in many other parts of the world. In a short time, most people gave up the old hunting and gathering way of life and settled down to become farmers. The farmers founded the first villages and towns.

In the Nile valley in Egypt, in the Tigris and Euphrates valleys in what is now Iraq, and in the Indus valley of Pakistan, people learned how to irrigate the valleys by moving water from the rivers to their fields. From about 5000 years ago, these valleys became centres of brilliant early civilizations.

Left: In developed countries, farm machinery has largely replaced workers and only a small proportion of the people work on farms.

ANIMAL FARMING

Domesticated animals such as cattle, sheep, goats, pigs and chickens supply high quality protein in the form of milk or meat. They also provide wool, and hides for leather. More importantly in the developing countries cattle, such as oxen and buffalo, also provide power.

Traditionally farm animals feed by grazing, often using land that is unsuitable for crop cultivation. Nowadays in the West many animals are factory farmed. They are housed in special units and fed on manufactured foods.

Farming in Temperate Lands

Farms near cities in temperate countries produce fresh food for city-dwellers. These farms are called market gardens (truck farms in the USA). This is a type of intensive farming. Intensive farming is important in densely populated countries. By contrast, ranching is a kind of extensive farming. Extensive farms are usually on land which is unsuitable for intensive crop growing. Another type of farming is called mixed farming. Mixed farms produce crops and animal products.

Working Together

In some countries, groups of farmers choose to work together through co-operatives. On co-operatives farmers work together, and share the produce. Collective farms in many communist countries, such as the *sovkhozy* (government-owned farms) in the USSR, are similar except that people here work for a wage.

Below: In developing countries, ancient farming methods survive. Here, an Archimedes screw is used to extract water from the River Nile to irrigate farmland.

Forestry

In North America, northern Europe and the USSR, forestry is highly mechanized. Lumberjacks fell trees with powersaws and felling machines. Many of the trunks are transported from the logging camps to rivers, where they are floated downstream to a sawmill. Some heavy hardwoods will not float. They must be transported by road or rail.

Wood is a valuable product. It is used in buildings, furniture, paper making and as a fuel. It also has many less obvious uses, as in the manufacture of such things as explosives, manmade fibres and medicines.

Forests cover about one-third of the world's surface. The *coniferous* (evergreen) *forests* are most widespread in the northern hemisphere. They contain cedars, firs, pines and spruces that are adapted to survive long, cold winters. These commercially valuable trees are also called *softwoods*, because most species are easy to saw. The leading softwood producers are the USSR, the USA and Canada.

Temperate hardwood forests contain such deciduous trees as ash, beech, chestnut, elm, hickory, oak and willow, which shed their leaves in autumn. A third type of forest is

Above: The most valuable tropical hardwoods are usually scattered throughout the dense forests. This makes their extraction difficult. In southern Asia elephants are often used to drag the tree trunks through the forest to rivers or loading sites.

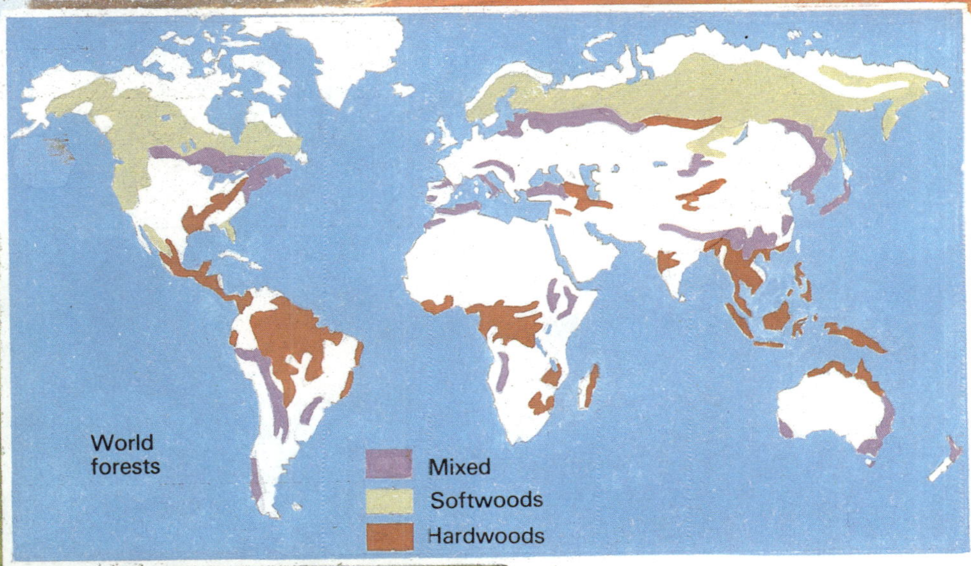

Left: The map shows that the world's main softwood forests are in the northern hemisphere — in North America, Scandinavia and the USSR. In some areas, these forests merge southwards into mixed forests and, eventually, deciduous (hardwood) forests. The largest hardwood forests, however, are in the tropics, especially the Amazon basin, central Africa and South-East Asia.

the *mixed forest* zone between the coniferous and hardwood forests. The fourth type of forest, the tropical hardwood forest, contains such trees as ebony, mahogany and teak.

Foresters in the northern coniferous forests replace the trees they cut down with young saplings. However, in recent years, acid rain has been killing many trees. Acid rain is formed when raindrops dissolve harmful gases emitted from factories and power stations.

The huge tropical hardwood forests are being destroyed even faster. The trees are cut down and burnt, to create grazing space for cattle, or for farming. However once the land is cleared the soil rapidly deteriorates and becomes unsuitable for farming or grazing, and another area of forest must be cut down. Every year an area of tropical forest the size of England is destroyed.

Harvest of the Sea

Fish is a valuable food. In some countries, including Japan and Norway, it makes up about one-tenth of people's diets. Freshwater fish form about one-tenth of the world's total catch of 75 million tonnes. The richest ocean fishing grounds are in the north-western Pacific Ocean and in the north-eastern Atlantic Ocean. More fish are caught in the shallow waters of the continental shelves than in the deep ocean waters.

Traditionally, fishermen were hunters, who were never sure of a good catch. Today, however, modern technology is aiding fishermen. For example, radar and sonic depth finders are used to locate shoals of fish.

The use of modern methods has led to overfishing in some areas. This had led to a search for new food products from the oceans. For example, krill, a shrimp-like creature, is found in great quantities around Antarctica. It could be harvested as a food for human consumption, but care must be taken that this does not create a deficit for the seabirds, seals and whales that rely on it as their major food source.

WHALING

For centuries whales have been hunted for their meat, bone and blubber, their huge bodies providing the material for an assortment of goods, ranging from lipstick to fishing rods, shoes to cooking fat. As one species of whale became harder to find because it was over-hunted, and becoming extinct, another, more abundant species would be hunted, so that one type of whale after another became almost extinct.

As early as the 1930s attempts were made to regulate the number of whales killed for commercial use, but it was not until the late 1970s that these regulations were strictly enforced, due to a massive "Save the Whale" campaign. All the products that had been obtained from whales could now be procured from other sources.

Throughout the 1980s some countries ignored the world ban, but nowadays fewer whales are killed for commercial reasons.

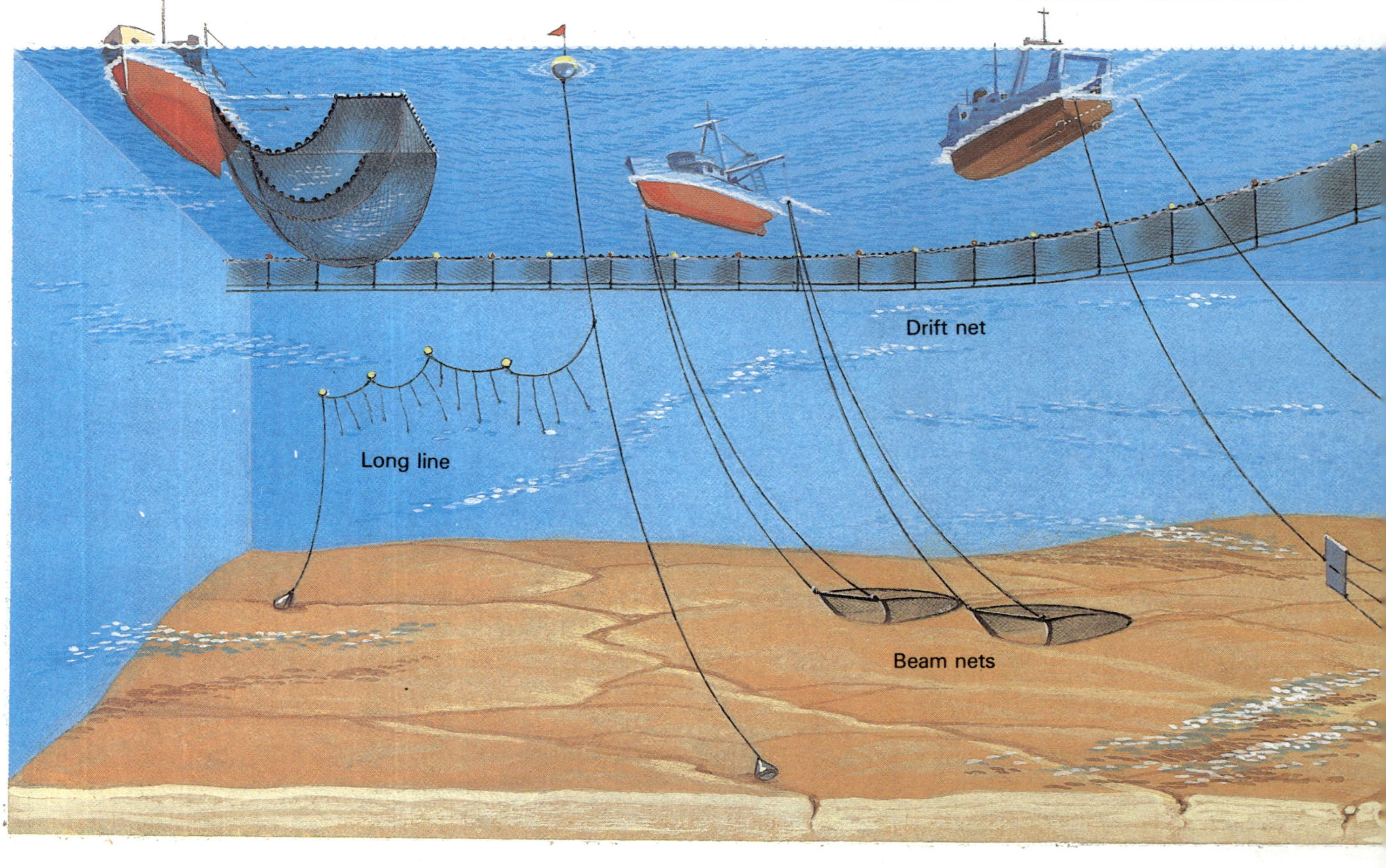

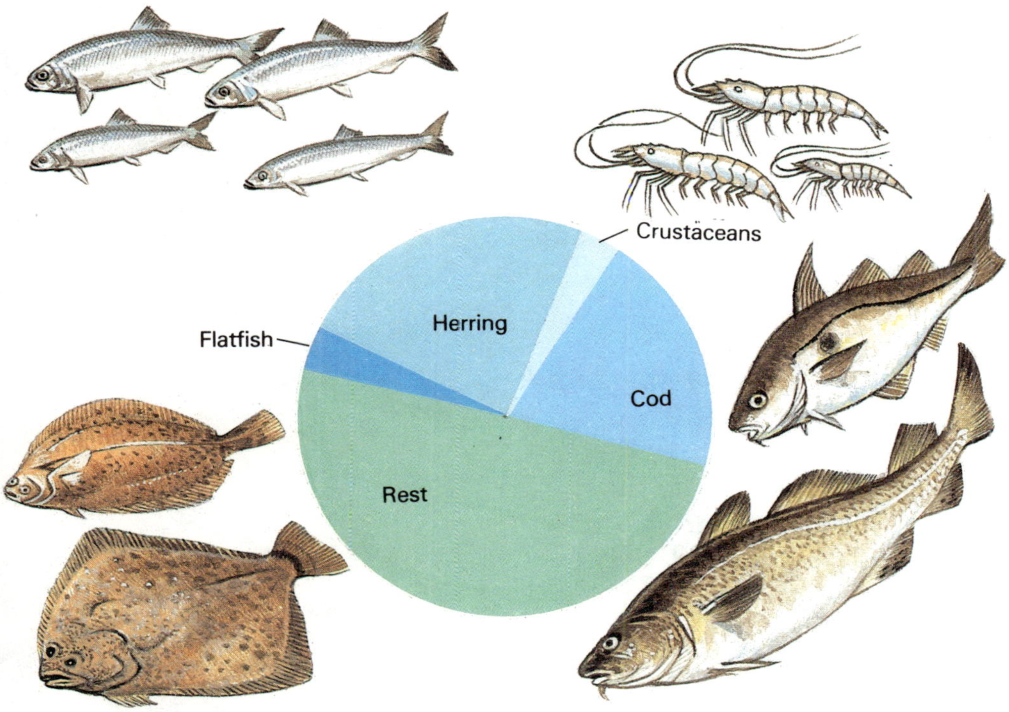

Above: The diagram shows the proportions of various fishes and crustaceans caught around the world. The chief fishing nation is Japan. It accounts for about one-seventh of the world's total catch.

Fish Farming

Attempts are now being made to conserve fish and to develop fish farms. The breeding and raising of fish in tanks and ponds is called aquaculture. Carp have been raised in China for thousands of years, and oysters have been bred in Europe since Roman times.

Today, many species of freshwater fish, including carp, eels and trout are successfully raised. And young salmon are reared in fresh water and later moved to salt water. This mimics the conditions experienced by wild salmon which migrate from rivers to the oceans. The farming of saltwater fish is generally less economic, but overfishing in the oceans is making scientists study saltwater fish farming.

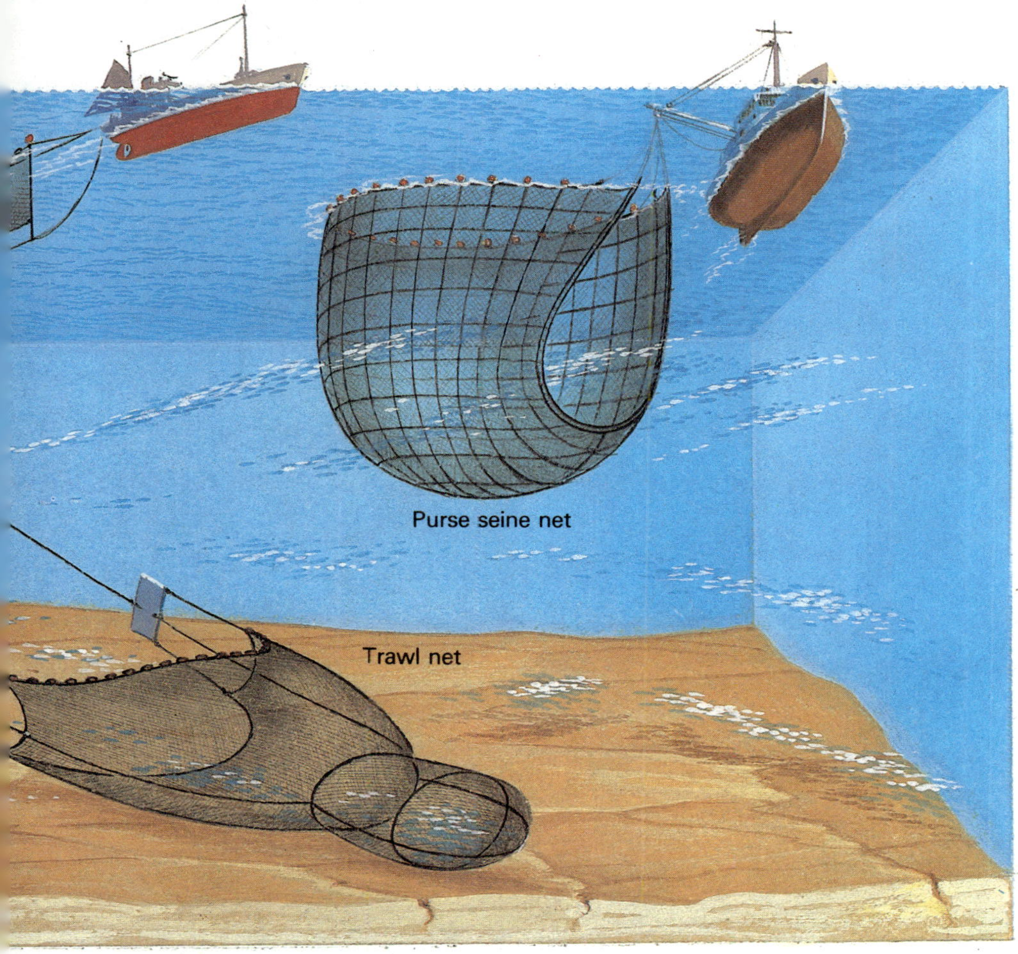

Left: The diagram shows various techniques used in the fishing industry. Long-lining involves putting out long, or ground, lines. Attached to them are short lines with baited hooks. This technique is used to catch tuna.

Drift or gill nets are held up by floats. The gills of fish which try to swim through the nets are caught in the mesh. Many herrings and mackerel are caught by drift nets.

Drag or trawl nets are large, bag-shaped nets which are dragged along the seabed at depths as great as 1000 metres. These nets are used to catch flatfish and other bottom-living fish and crustaceans.

Purse seine nets are used when shoals of such fishes as sardines and herrings are located on the ship's radar. The purse seine nets are then drawn around the shoal.

Pacific shrimp boats haul two beam nets across the sea floor. They catch prawns and shrimps. Many catcher boats now work with a mother factory ship. Instead of returning to port, they deliver their catch to a large factory ship. There the fish are rapidly processed and frozen.

Peoples of the World

People belong to the species *Homo sapiens* (intelligent man). They first appeared around 50,000 years ago. They displaced the closely related Neanderthal people, who died out around the end of the Ice Age.

People vary in appearance. Many of these differences are probably adaptations to the varied climatic conditions in which the people developed. The human family is divided into four main sub-groups: Caucasoids, Mongoloids, Negroids and Australoids.

Caucasoids include the mostly fair-skinned people of Europe and the many people of European origin in other continents. The Arabs of North Africa and most of the much darker skinned people of north-eastern Africa, south-western Asia and India are also Caucasoids.

Mongoloids, with the yellowish skin and straight, dark hair, include most of the people of eastern Asia, Eskimos and American Indians. Negroids include the Black people of Africa and Black Americans, the descendants of Black African slaves.

Australoids include Australian Aborigines, the Veddoids of southern India and the Ainu, the first inhabitants of Japan.

Below: Examples of members of the human family. Most Europeans, Arabs and most people in south-western Asia and India are Caucasoids. Australian Aborigines belong to the Australoid sub-group. The Negroid group includes Black Africans and Black Americans. The Mongoloid sub-group includes most people in eastern Asia and the American Indians. Members of the sub-groups have intermarried. For example, many Mexicans are mestizos, of mixed European and American Indian descent.

Above: The first North Americans came from Asia, perhaps 40,000 years ago, during the Ice Age. The sea level was then much lower than it is today and a land bridge connected northern Asia and North America. These Mongoloid people were the ancestors of the American Indians.

Ways of Life

The ways of life of people still vary greatly around the world. There are still a few people, including the Bushmen and pygmies of Africa, who live much like our ancestors before the invention of agriculture. They live by hunting animals and gathering seeds and roots. Other people are farmers, though many farmers in Africa, Asia and South America are poor. But more and more people are making their homes in cities and towns. Their chief jobs in the developed western countries are in manufacturing and service industries.

Ideas and Beliefs

Different beliefs are important in different places. For some people religion is a very important part of their lives. For others political beliefs, such as communism or socialism, are more important. Whereas in the past there was a tendency to see one's own belief as the only true way of life, nowadays more and more people are tolerant of other people's views, and live in harmony together.

LANGUAGES

There are about 3000 languages and many more dialects. Many have large vocabularies and a written form. Others contain comparatively few words and have no written form.

Some languages are closely related to each other. French, Italian, Portuguese and Spanish all come from Latin, the language of ancient Rome. These languages form the Romance language group. This group belongs to a wider family of languages, called the Indo-European family. This is the world's largest family, followed by the Sino-Tibetan, which includes Chinese.

Some languages have spread around the world. The chief international language is English. French, German and Spanish are also spoken widely throughout the world.

Nations of the World

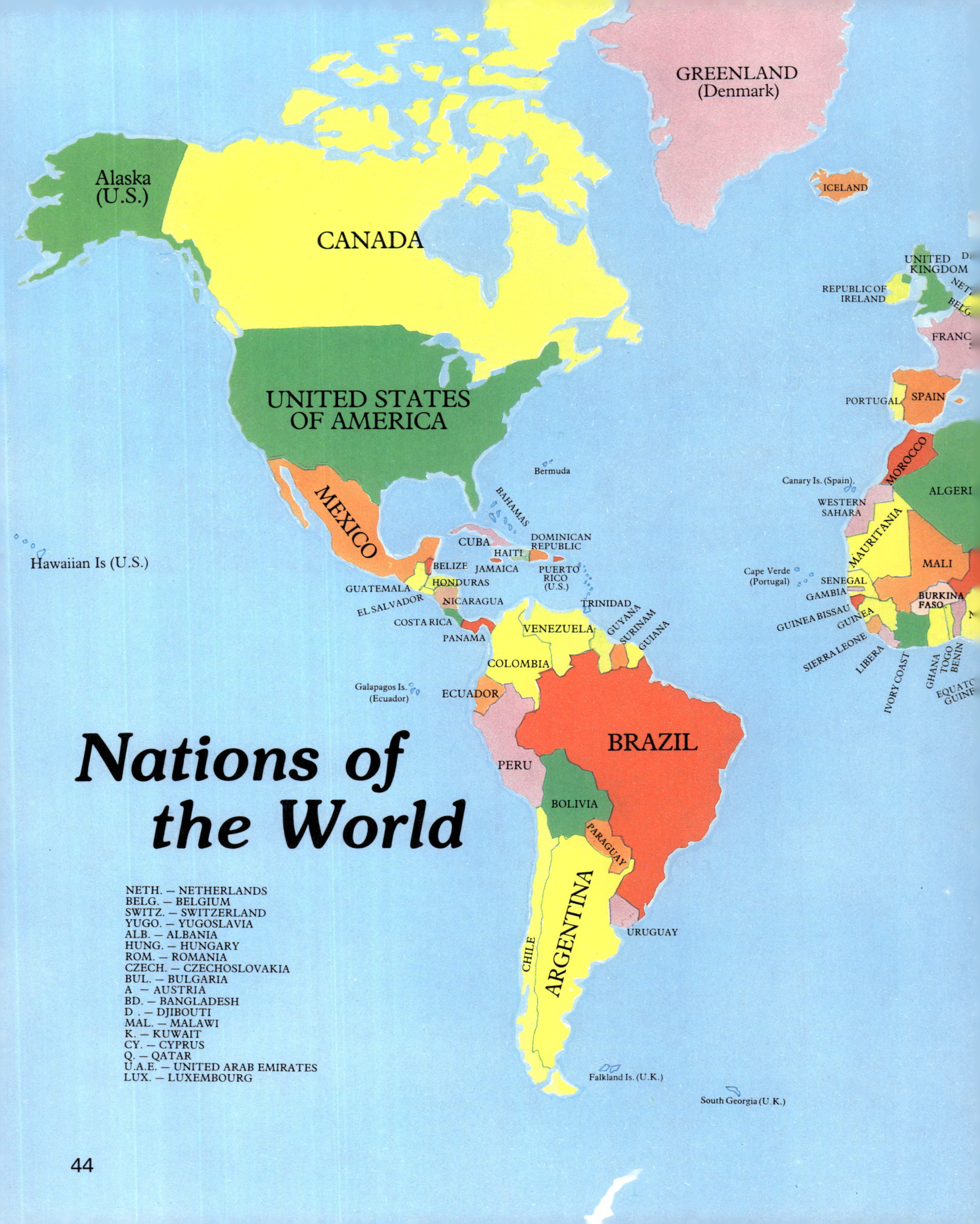

NETH. — NETHERLANDS
BELG. — BELGIUM
SWITZ. — SWITZERLAND
YUGO. — YUGOSLAVIA
ALB. — ALBANIA
HUNG. — HUNGARY
ROM. — ROMANIA
CZECH. — CZECHOSLOVAKIA
BUL. — BULGARIA
A — AUSTRIA
BD. — BANGLADESH
D . — DJIBOUTI
MAL. — MALAWI
K. — KUWAIT
CY. — CYPRUS
Q. — QATAR
U.A.E. — UNITED ARAB EMIRATES
LUX. — LUXEMBOURG

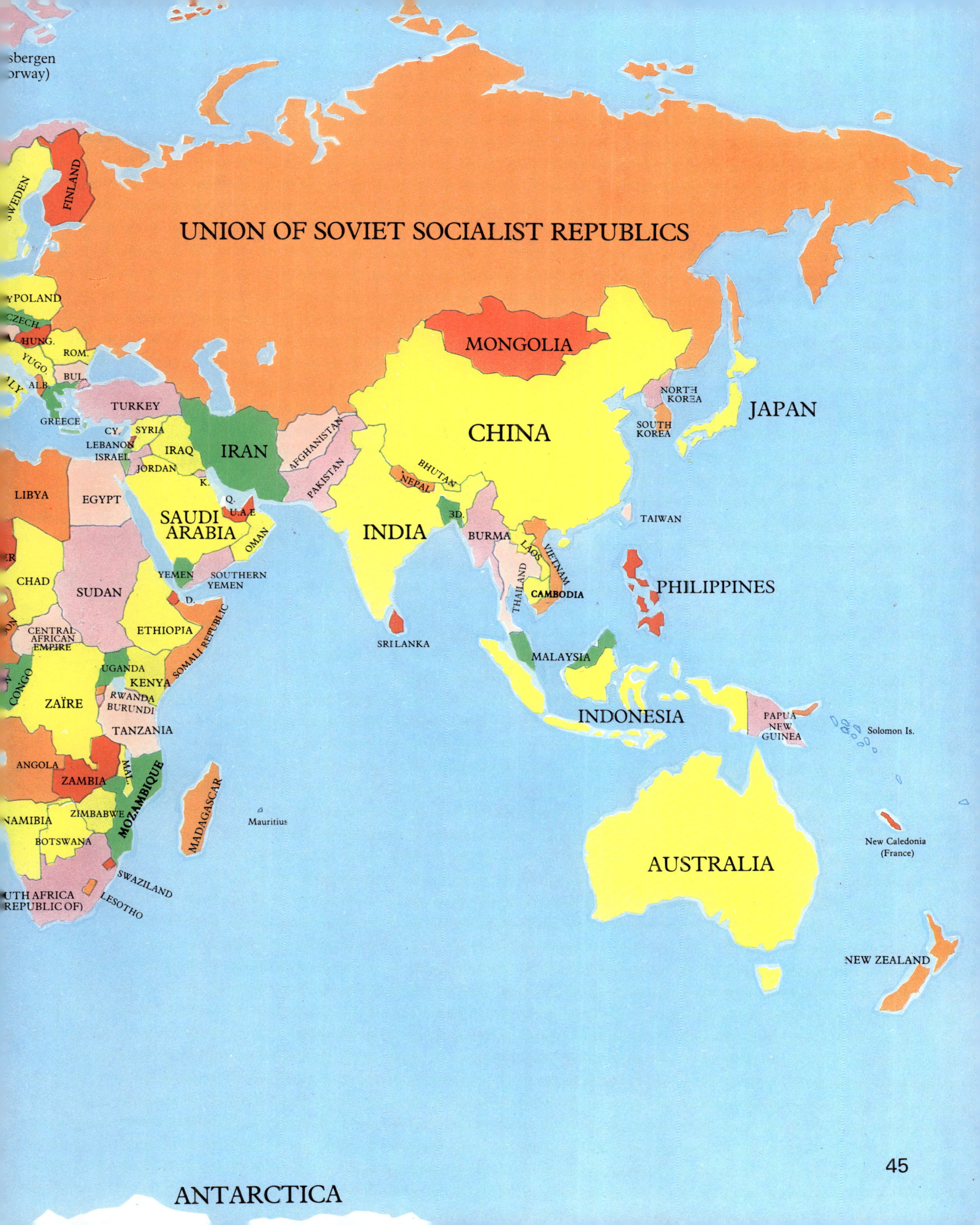
sbergen
orway)
UNION OF SOVIET SOCIALIST REPUBLICS
FINLAND
WEDEN
POLAND
CZECH.
HUNG.
ROM.
YUGO.
BUL.
ALB.
LY
TURKEY
GREECE
CY.
SYRIA
LEBANON
ISRAEL
IRAQ
JORDAN
IRAN
K.
Q.
U.A.E.
AFGHANISTAN
PAKISTAN
MONGOLIA
CHINA
NORTH KOREA
SOUTH KOREA
JAPAN
BHUTAN
NEPAL
BD.
INDIA
BURMA
LAOS
VIETNAM
THAILAND
CAMBODIA
TAIWAN
PHILIPPINES
SRI LANKA
MALAYSIA
INDONESIA
PAPUA NEW GUINEA
Solomon Is.
LIBYA
EGYPT
SAUDI ARABIA
OMAN
YEMEN
SOUTHERN YEMEN
CHAD
SUDAN
D.
ETHIOPIA
SOMALI REPUBLIC
CENTRAL AFRICAN EMPIRE
CONGO
UGANDA
KENYA
ZAÏRE
RWANDA
BURUNDI
TANZANIA
ANGOLA
ZAMBIA
MAL.
MOZAMBIQUE
ZIMBABWE
NAMIBIA
BOTSWANA
MADAGASCAR
Mauritius
SWAZILAND
LESOTHO
UTH AFRICA
REPUBLIC OF)
AUSTRALIA
New Caledonia
(France)
NEW ZEALAND
ANTARCTICA

Index

Illustrators
Mike Atkinson, Jim Dugdale, Ron Jobson
and Roger Payne.

Cover illustrations by
Brian Watson/Linden Artists

 Published in Great Britain by Cliveden Press, an Egmont Company, Egmont House, PO Box 111, Great Ducie Street, Manchester M60 3BL.

Printed in Singapore.

ISBN 0 7498 0398 3

Reprinted 1992

THE WORLD OF

Nature

THE WORLD OF
Nature

CLIVEDEN PRESS

Contents

Above: Freshwater insects are eaten by small fishes such as minnows. They in turn are eaten by larger fishes such as trout, as well as by birds like the kingfisher. This is a simple food chain.

The Balance of Nature

In the wild, plants and animals depend on each other for survival. Most plants make their own food with the help of energy from the sun. Animals, on the other hand, must eat plants or other animals to obtain the energy they need. The process by which energy is passed from one creature to another is called a food chain. Thus plants use the sun's energy to produce food from simple materials. Animals called herbivores eat the plants, and they themselves are eaten by carnivorous animals. If the numbers in any part of the chain rise or fall dramatically, this affects other links in the chain. Thus if a crop fails, the herbivores starve and fewer predators will survive. This is part of the process called the balance of nature.

Food chains are not always as simple as this. The carnivore may eat many types of prey and may itself be eaten by several other types of predator. When several food chains become interconnected in this way they form a food web.

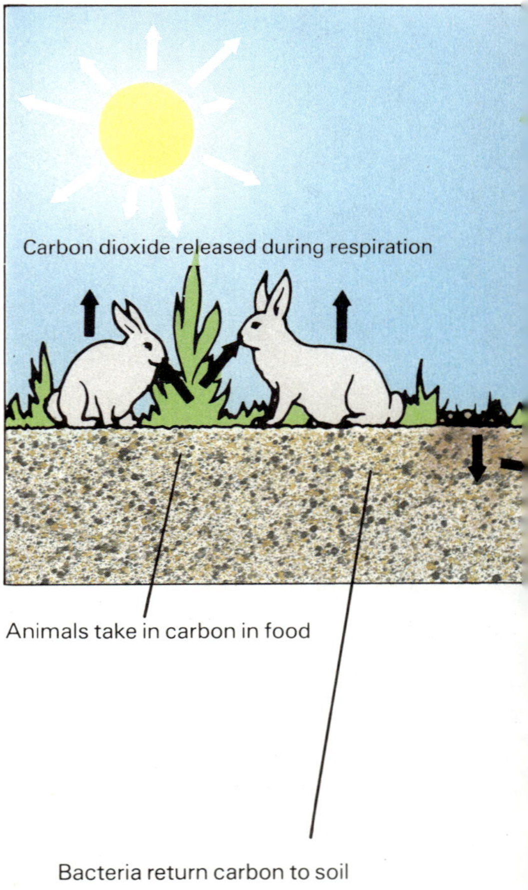

CARBON CYCLE

All living things contain carbon. As much as 18 per cent of all living material is carbon, so it is a very important chemical. Carbon is never lost but is always recycled.

All living things breathe out carbon dioxide, and plants use the gas to make food when they photosynthesize. When the plant is eaten by an animal, the carbon is taken into its body. Later on, the animal returns some of the carbon to the atmosphere when it breathes out carbon dioxide. When an animal or plant dies, the carbon in its body is again returned to the atmosphere, this time through the action of bacteria. In this way the carbon is recycled through the environment and very little is lost.

Below: When rabbits eat plants they take in carbon but, like all living things, they release it as carbon dioxide when they breathe out. Plants take carbon dioxide in again when they photosynthesize, and in this way the carbon is recycled.

Animal Populations

The numbers of animals and plants remain fairly constant from year to year. There are several factors which keep their populations in check. First the amount of food available is often limited, so the more animals there are, the less food there is to go round. If the numbers of an animal suddenly increase for some reason then the numbers of its predators soon increase as well. This gradually brings the numbers down again.

Sometimes the controls fail and numbers of a species increase unchecked. If they affect man they are called pests. In many cases man has upset the balance of nature and brought about the population explosion without realizing it.

Many insects feed on plants, but will often feed on only a few species. In the wild, the plants are generally spaced out. This spacing out helps to keep the insect population at a steady level.

But if the insect finds an area where its foodplant is abundant its numbers will soon rise. Man often grows vast areas of crops for food. As a result those insects that can eat the crop benefit and soon become pests.

Above: The Colorado beetle can become a serious pest of man's crops. It is particularly fond of potatoes and if not controlled can devastate a whole harvest.

Man often controls pests by spraying them with chemicals. But sometimes he can use natural agents as a form of biological control. Rabbits have been controlled by the introduction of a disease called myxomatosis which is transmitted by fleas. In recent years, however, many rabbits have become immune to myxomatosis.

Ichneumon wasps also make good agents of control since they lay their eggs in other insects and eventually kill them.

Right: The mongoose is skilled at catching wary prey such as the black rat. It helps keep down the numbers of rats and acts as a natural 'control' agent.

The Hidden Past

Fossils are evidence found in rocks of animals and plants which once lived on Earth. They range from animal footprints to animal bones, plants turned to stone and insects preserved in amber.

The pictures above show how a fossil is formed. When an animal dies (1), it must be buried quickly in underwater sediments. The flesh soon decays, but the bones survive (2).

Why Fossils are Important

Fossils occur in rocks all over the world. Because rock layers are folded and pushed upwards, fossils of seashells are found even at the tops of mountains. The study of fossils helps geologists to date rocks. It also helps us to understand the evolution of plants and animals throughout Earth history.

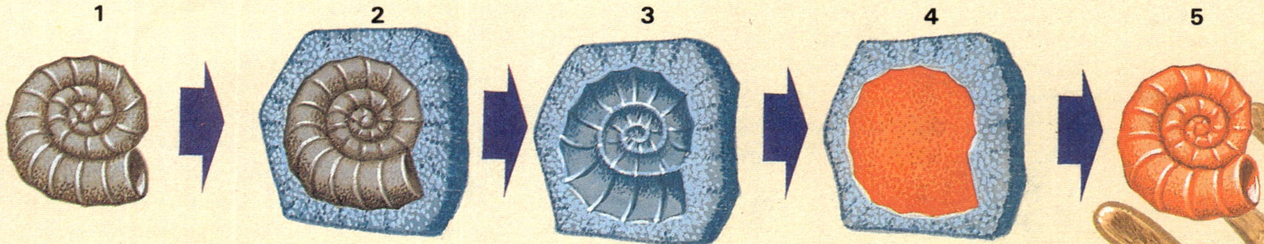

Above: The diagram shows how fossil moulds and casts are formed. A dead ammonite (1) is buried by sediment. The sediment is slowly compressed into rock (2). Water seeping through the rock dissolves the ammonite. This cavity is a mould of the ammonite (3). Later, minerals may be deposited from water in the cavity (4) to produce a fossil cast (5).

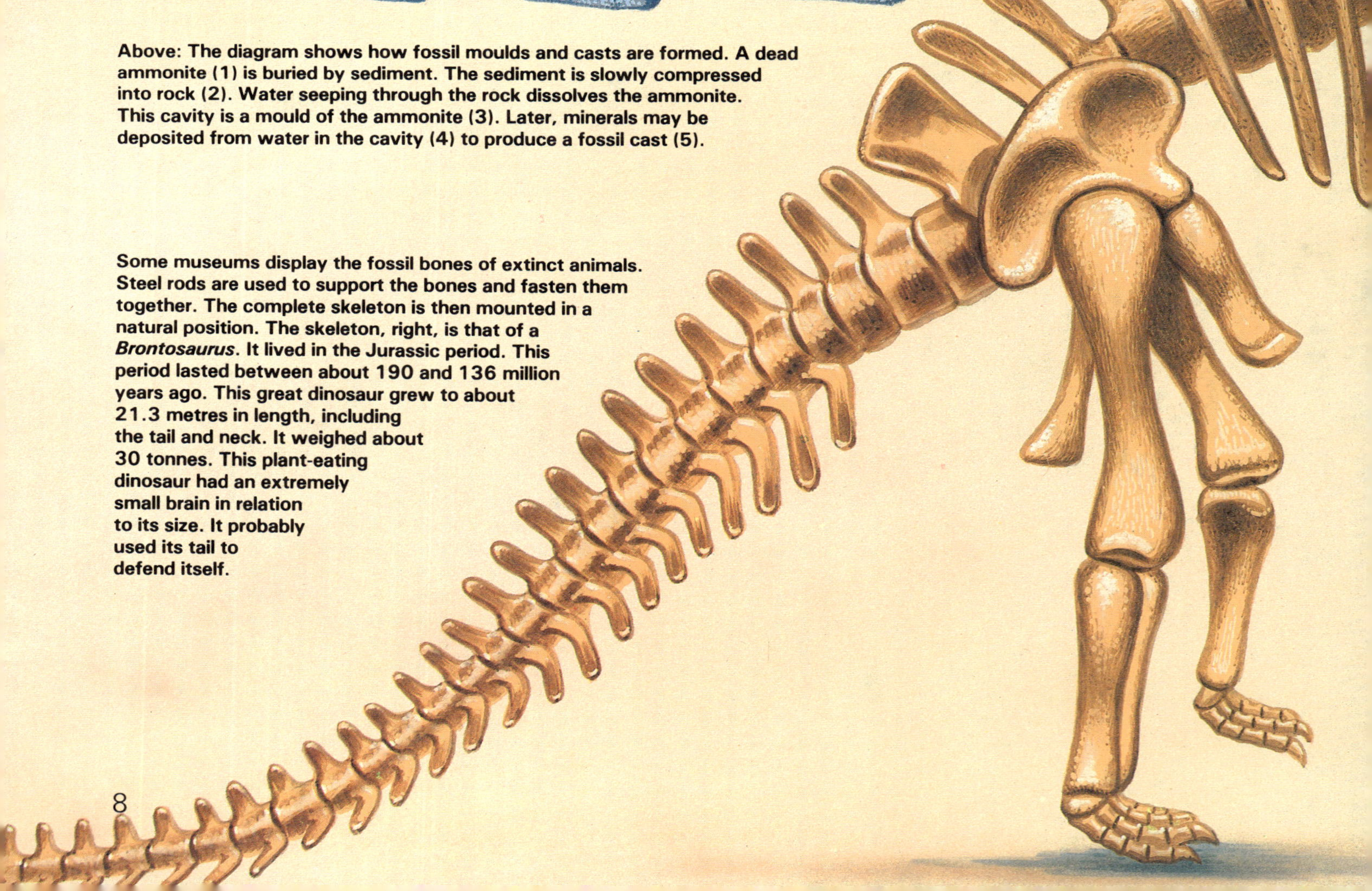

Some museums display the fossil bones of extinct animals. Steel rods are used to support the bones and fasten them together. The complete skeleton is then mounted in a natural position. The skeleton, right, is that of a *Brontosaurus*. It lived in the Jurassic period. This period lasted between about 190 and 136 million years ago. This great dinosaur grew to about 21.3 metres in length, including the tail and neck. It weighed about 30 tonnes. This plant-eating dinosaur had an extremely small brain in relation to its size. It probably used its tail to defend itself.

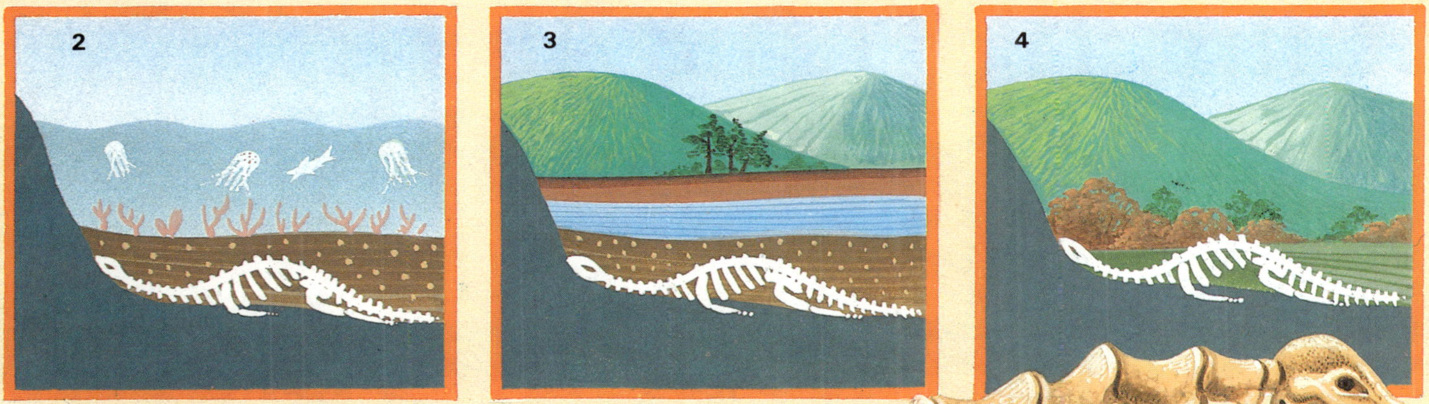

The sediments are pressed into hard rock. Minerals penetrate the buried bones, turning them into stone (3). Millions of years later, the rocks are raised up and worn down, revealing the fossil (4).

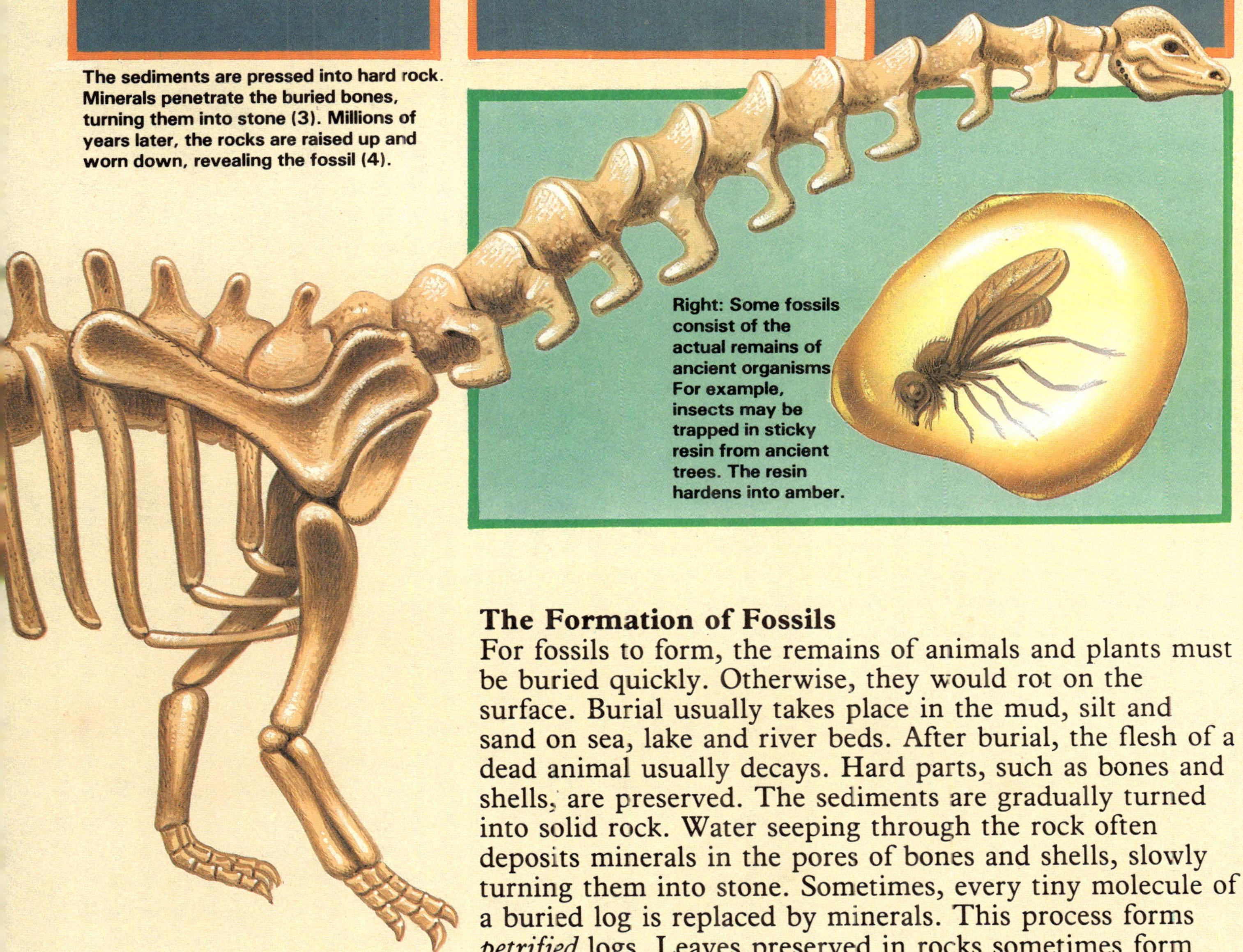

Right: Some fossils consist of the actual remains of ancient organisms. For example, insects may be trapped in sticky resin from ancient trees. The resin hardens into amber.

The Formation of Fossils

For fossils to form, the remains of animals and plants must be buried quickly. Otherwise, they would rot on the surface. Burial usually takes place in the mud, silt and sand on sea, lake and river beds. After burial, the flesh of a dead animal usually decays. Hard parts, such as bones and shells, are preserved. The sediments are gradually turned into solid rock. Water seeping through the rock often deposits minerals in the pores of bones and shells, slowly turning them into stone. Sometimes, every tiny molecule of a buried log is replaced by minerals. This process forms *petrified* logs. Leaves preserved in rocks sometimes form thin films of carbon which show the shape of the leaf.

Other fossils are moulds or casts of the original hard parts (see the diagrams on the facing page). A few fossils include the actual bodies of animals, such as woolly mammoths which lived 30,000 years ago. These have been preserved in the frozen ground of Siberia. But such fossils are extremely rare.

A person compared in size with Brontosaurus

Animals of Long Ago

Animals have lived on Earth for millions of years. Scientists know about them because their remains are found embedded in rocks, turned to stone. These stony remains are called *fossils*.

Nobody knows exactly when life first appeared, because there are very few fossils older than about 570 million years, the start of what is called the *Palaeozoic Era*. Palaeozoic comes from Greek words meaning 'old life'. Scientists can put approximate dates to fossils because they can work out the age of the rocks in which they are found. Fossils show how plants and animals have changed, or evolved, throughout the Earth's long history.

Below: Some of the dinosaurs, the giant reptiles which dominated the Earth for millions of years. Alamosaurus was one of several huge beasts feeding only on plants, while Tyrannosaurus was a fierce, meat-eating predator. By contrast, Compsognathus was about the size of a turkey.

The Pageant of Life

The first animals were *invertebrates*, animals that have no backbones, and they lived in the sea. They were soft, primitive creatures, rather like the jellyfish and sponges of today. The first animals with backbones – *vertebrates* – appeared about 450 million years ago. They were primitive forms of fish. After a long time some fish became able to breathe air and developed lungs (there are still some lungfishes today). From them came the first animals that could live both on land and in water. These *amphibians* were the ancestors of present-day frogs. They lived about 350 million years ago.

Many kinds of life evolved on land, including insects and reptiles. By about 200 million years ago giant reptiles, the dinosaurs, ruled the Earth. They died out suddenly, about 65 million years ago. By then birds and mammals had evolved, and mammals became the dominant animals. Man is one of the most recent mammals to evolve. Our ancestors appeared about two million years ago.

Below: A panorama of life through prehistoric time, from the first forms of life in the sea, through the age of the dinosaurs, to the present-day age of mammals.

Below: The flying creature in the picture was Archaeopteryx. This strange animal may have been the world's first bird. It lived 150 million years ago in parts of Europe. Scientists now think that its primitive wings were not strong enough to lift it far off the ground, so it may have hopped and fluttered instead.

Records in Nature

HIGHEST MOUNTAINS (metres)

Above: During the Earth's long history, many mountain ranges have been created by movements in the rocks, and then gradually worn away by water, wind and ice. The highest peaks today are in the youngest mountain ranges – the Himalayas, Andes, Rockies and Alps. There may well have been higher mountain peaks millions of years ago.

There is a great range in the size of living things. At one end of the scale there are viruses – organisms on the very borders of life – which are too small to be seen without the aid of powerful electron microscopes. At the other extreme there is the blue whale which can weigh over 120 tonnes, and the Californian redwood tree which grows as high as a 35-storey building.

The life-span of living things also varies greatly. Small insects, such as the mayfly, have an adult life-span which can be measured in days or even hours, while the tortoise may live for 150 years or more. Some plants, especially trees, live far longer. There are giant sequoia trees in California which began life almost 4,000 years ago, and bristlecone pines which are as old as the pyramids.

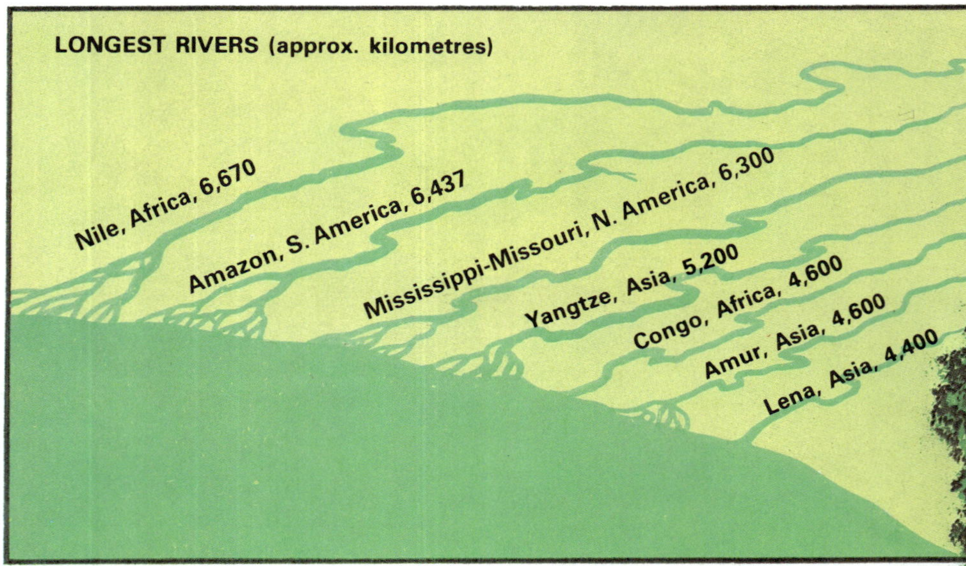

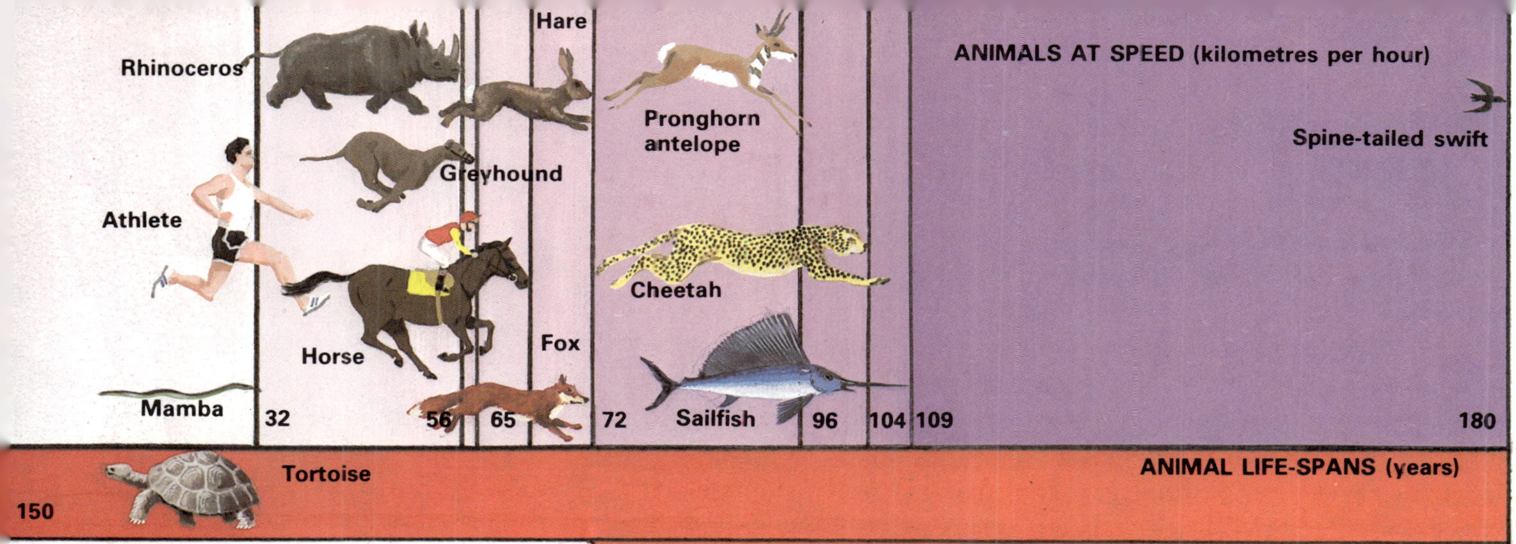

The table shows the average maximum life-spans of various animals. It is based upon records of animals in captivity. Animals in the wild have shorter life-spans.

The speed at which animals move is often difficult to measure accurately, but there is no doubt about the record holder. The spine-tailed swift can fly at more than 180 km/h. The fastest land animal is the cheetah, which can exceed 100 km/h over short distances. The proverbial tortoise does well to reach 1 km/h.

The Plant Kingdom

There are nearly half a million species of plants on the earth. With the exception of some primitive types, they all need three basic ingredients to survive: air, light and water. Plants are found in almost every type of habitat, including most of the surface waters of the world's rivers, lakes and oceans. Most species live in temperate and tropical regions but plants are extremely adaptable, and have even conquered such inhospitable environments as hot mineral springs and dry deserts with little rainfall.

How Plants Live

Although there is a great variety in the shape, size and appearance of plants, all of them, apart from fungi and bacteria, make their own food using simple raw materials and energy from the sun. They trap the sun's rays using the green pigment chlorophyll, and combine water and carbon dioxide (a gas present in the air) to make simple sugars. They also release oxygen into the air — which all living things need for respiration. This process, known as photosynthesis, is vital to the survival of all life on earth.

Plants include some of the smallest things as well as the largest. The surface waters of ponds and lakes teem with microscopic algae, many of which exist as just a single cell. By contrast, the giant redwood trees of California may grow over 90 metres tall.

Some plants reproduce so rapidly that new individuals are produced within minutes by simple division, whereas the bristlecone pine trees live to be more than 3,500 years old. Each year they still produce a new crop of seedlings.

Almost all types of plants are eaten by one species of animal or another. Animals that eat plants are called herbivores, and they include such creatures as cows and locusts. Other animals eat only meat and these are called carnivores. However, the animals that they prey upon will have eaten plants. If it were not for plants, animal life could not exist on earth.

Right: This evolutionary 'tree' shows how the different groups of plants have evolved throughout the geological ages.

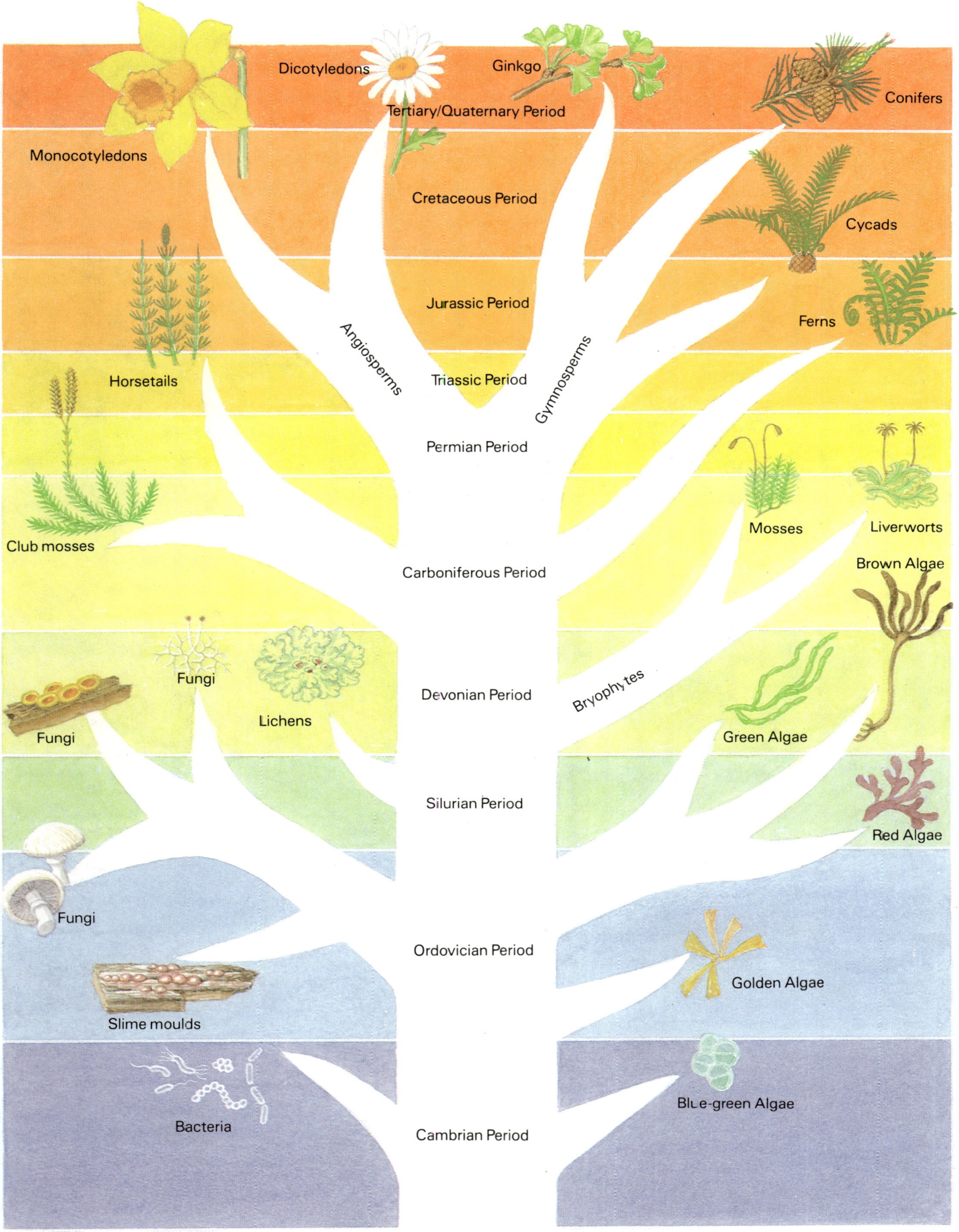
Dicotyledons
Ginkgo
Conifers
Tertiary/Quaternary Period
Monocotyledons
Cretaceous Period
Cycads
Jurassic Period
Ferns
Angiosperms
Triassic Period
Gymnosperms
Horsetails
Permian Period
Mosses
Liverworts
Club mosses
Carboniferous Period
Brown Algae
Fungi
Lichens
Devonian Period
Bryophytes
Fungi
Green Algae
Silurian Period
Red Algae
Fungi
Ordovician Period
Golden Algae
Slime moulds
Blue-green Algae
Bacteria
Cambrian Period

Lowly Plants

The lowly plants have existed on earth for much longer than the flowering plants we grow in our gardens. Many have remained almost unchanged for millions of years. They generally have a simple structure and, with the exception of ferns, do not have supporting fibres. This means that they cannot grow to any great size.

Most of the lowly plants contain the green pigment chlorophyll. This helps them to trap sunlight energy and make their own food. The exceptions are the bacteria and fungi which have to use other sources of food such as the dead bodies of plants or animals, and are responsible for decay.

Advanced plants mostly have flowers and produce seeds in order to reproduce. Lowly plants, however, often reproduce by means of spores. The bacteria and many of the algae reproduce by simple division, and like the rest of the lowly plants they need damp conditions.

Left: Mushrooms and toadstools are the reproductive parts of fungi. Most of the fungus lives underground forming a complex web of thread-like strands called a mycelium.

The spores of fungi are always present in the air. They grow and thrive when food, such as bread, is left in damp conditions, forming patches of mould.

Algae

Algae are the simplest forms of true plant life. They possess chlorophyll, but many contain other pigments, giving them many colours. They range from simple, single-celled plants which make ponds appear green, to immense seaweeds, several metres long.

Fungi

Unlike algae, fungi cannot make their own food and depend on a ready-made source. Many feed on dead matter and cause decay.

Lichens are strange plants which are the result of a partnership between algae and fungi. The relationship is called 'symbiotic', and both partners benefit from it. Their growth is very slow.

Mosses and Liverworts

Mosses and liverworts are simple plants which lack true roots and stems. They are restricted to damp habitats and reproduce by spores produced in capsules.

Ferns

Ferns are generally long-lived plants. They have a rootstock and a strong, supporting stem which can conduct water and dissolved food substances. This means that they can often reach a large size. They still produce spores during reproduction and depend on water for part of their life cycle.

Below: Fern spores are spread by the wind

Above: Ferns come in a variety of forms. Some are rooted in the soil and grow to large sizes. Others colonize walls or even grow on other plants, but all need damp conditions.

Right: Seaweeds are algae which grow on rocky shores. Mosses are common on walls and in damp places.

Flowers

Rose

Flowers contain the male and female cells of a plant. For successful fertilization to take place, the pollen (male cells) from one plant has to reach the ovum (female cell) of another. However, plants have one basic problem—they are rooted to the ground. To overcome this, plants have evolved all sorts of ways of transferring the pollen.

Despite their unlikely appearance, grasses are true flowering plants which produce countless thousands of minute pollen grains that are carried by the wind. Not surprisingly, most end up in the wrong place but enough reach another grass flower to ensure their survival. More typical flowers have colourful petals and often a strong smell to attract insects. In return for a meal of nectar, the insects transfer the pollen to the next flowers which they visit.

Primrose

Flower Plan

Although some species of flowers sometimes contain only the male or the female cells, most contain both but go to great lengths to prevent self-fertilization.

Despite a great variety of appearances most flowers conform to a basic plan with sepals, colourful petals, stamens which produce the male cells called pollen, and a central stigma containing the female cell or ovule.

The parts of a flower

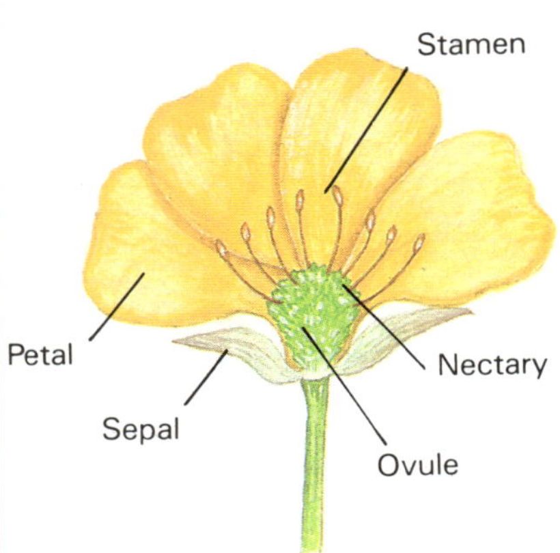

How a plant disperses its seeds

Above: Coconut seeds float in the sea.

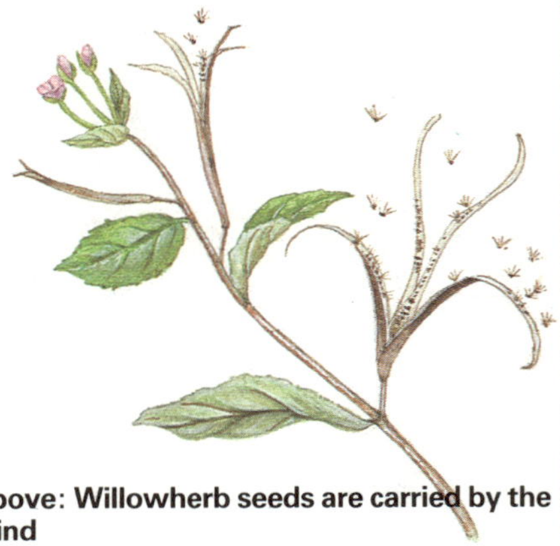

Above: Willowherb seeds are carried by the wind

Above: Burdock seeds have hooks which catch in the feathers and fur of animals.

Above: Poppy seeds are shaken from the pod.

How a seedling germinates and grows

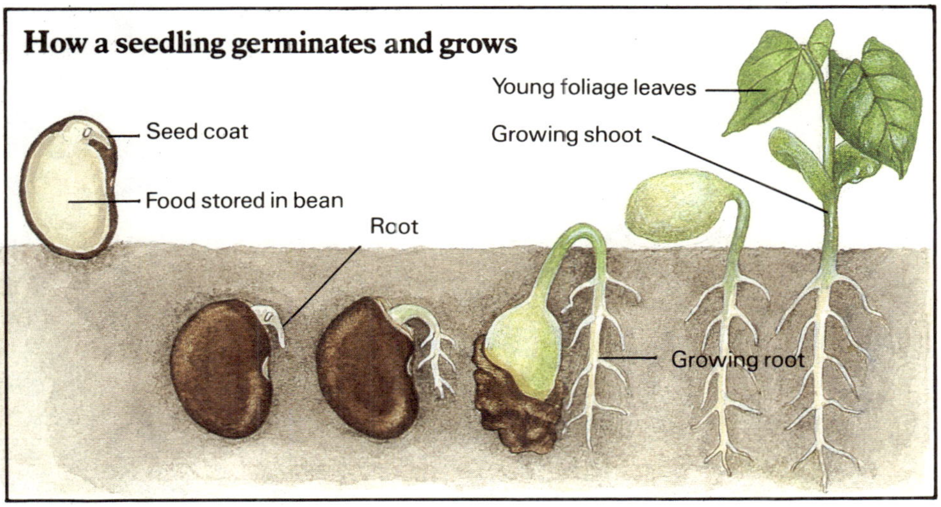

Above: Flowers occur in a whole variety of shapes, sizes and colours. They range from the inconspicuous flowers of grasses to the large and showy flowers of the sunflower. Some plants, such as the cactus, flower only briefly and irregularly, whereas others are in bloom for a full season—or even continuously.

Trees

Trees, woods and forests cover nearly one quarter of the earth's surface. They are a very important part of our environment, for they provide food, homes and shelter for a great variety of other living creatures. The key feature of all trees is their central woody stem or trunk. This grows as the tree grows, and provides support and protection.

Trees can broadly be split into those which drop their leaves each year (called deciduous trees) and those which do not (called evergreens). Many evergreens bear their seeds in cones and have needle-like leaves; these trees are called conifers. There are also some broadleaved trees, such as holly, which do not shed their leaves each autumn.

Palms are a special group of trees. Although they are deciduous, they are placed in a group of plants called monocotyledons, the group which also includes the grasses.

Above: The hazel is a deciduous tree. It has tiny female flowers, and male catkins which produce pollen. The seeds are encased in a tough shell, or nut.

Right: By counting the rings on a cross-section through a trunk you can estimate the age of a tree. Each ring roughly corresponds to a year's growth.

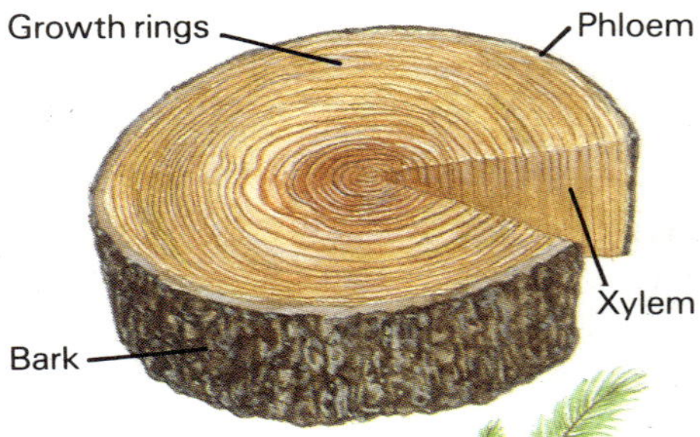

Below: There are many different types of tree throughout the world. Here are some typical species.

How Trees Grow

As well as providing support for the tree, the trunk carries the water supply for the leaves of the tree. Although the centre of the trunk is usually tough and woody, the outer tissues consist of tubes through which water is transported from the roots to the leaves. Some of this tissue also transports food from the leaves down to the roots and other parts of the tree. The trunk tissues are protected by the bark. If this is damaged, the tree may die.

Leaves are the vital life-supply for all plants. They produce food by photosynthesis, using the energy of sunlight to combine water and carbon dioxide. There are many different shapes of leaves, but all are designed to make best use of the available light.

In some parts of the world, the climate does not change during the year and the tree grows continuously. But elsewhere the climate varies, with either cold and hot seasons or dry and wet periods. The tree grows best in favourable conditions and, as a result, we can see growth rings in the trunk, each dark ring corresponding to a year's growth. In a good year the ring is thicker than in a poor year. By counting the number of rings, the age of the tree can be worked out.

In order that trees may reproduce, the female part of the flower must first be pollinated. In some trees, male and female parts are in the same flower. In others, they are in separate flowers or, sometimes, on separate male and female trees, such as holly.

Above: The spruce is a conifer with tiny flowers. The fertilized seeds grow and ripen in cones.

Right: An oak tree supports a whole community of plants and animals. Some animals feed on its leaves or acorns while others in turn prey upon them. Many beetles and fungi feed on the decaying wood and leaves.

Wonders of the Plant World

In the world of nature the Plant Kingdom has many unusual and fascinating species. From plants which can only be seen with the aid of a microscope to plants taller than a house, the Plant Kingdom is full of wonders.

We only have to think of fungi, those peculiar plants which can grow without the aid of sunlight and seem to pop out of the ground overnight, to realize that some plants are very odd. However, as we shall see, there are others which can confuse scientists even more!

Diatoms

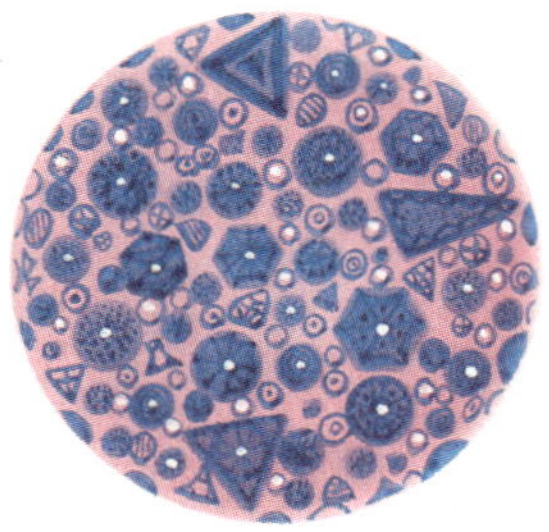

Volvox

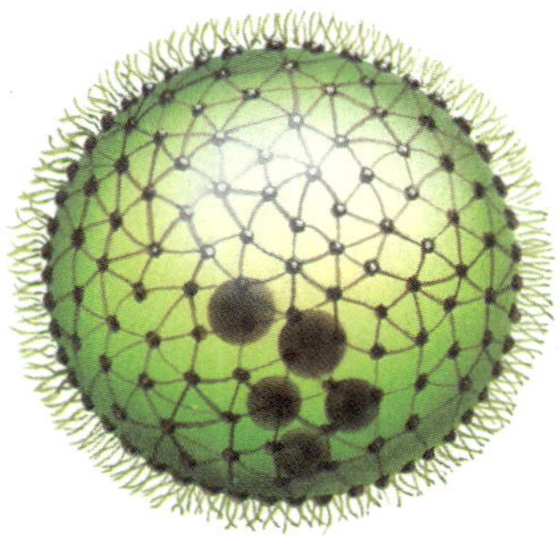

Lichen

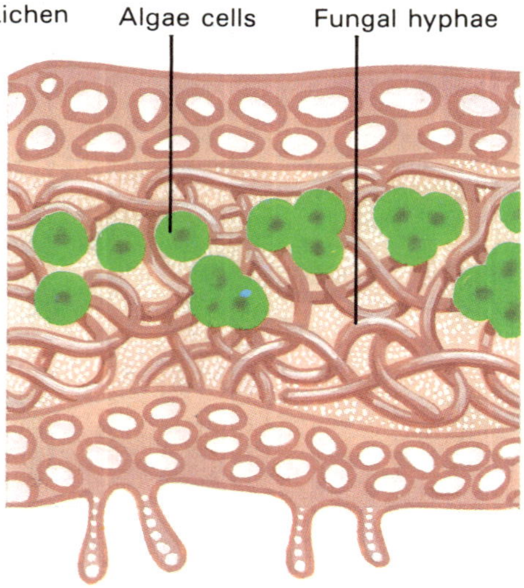

Left: Diatoms and colonies of single-celled algae like Volvox can move freely about in the water.

Right: This cross section through a plant stem shows how its water and minerals are absorbed by the suckers of mistletoe. Mistletoe grows on trees such as poplars.

Bottom left: Lichens are unusual plants made up of single-celled algae sandwiched between a fungus.

Lowly Plants

One of the ways that we normally use to tell animals from plants is by the fact that animals can move about, while plants stay fixed in one place. But among the group of primitive plants called the algae there are several species that can actually move about on their own.

Diatoms are tiny algae living within a silica shell, which can glide about in the water. Volvox is a plant which consists of a group of single-celled algae each of which has tiny hairs. By beating these Volvox can also move about in the water.

Flowering Plants

Among the flowering plants there are also many unusual species. Although most flowering plants make their own food by using the energy of sunlight trapped in their leaves, there are some kinds which 'steal' the minerals and food substances from other plants.

Dodder is a twining, parasitic plant whose stem sends suckers into the host plant.

Mistletoe is known as a partial parasite. It can make its own food using sunlight, but first it must rob a host plant of some vital minerals.

The most unusual flowering plants are the carnivorous species. They live in places, such as bogs, which lack the nitrogen they need for healthy growth. Therefore they catch insects and other small creatures in special traps (which are really special leaves) and absorb the nitrogen from their bodies.

Rafflesia

Giant redwood

Above: Rafflesia is the world's biggest flower. It can reach 60 centimetres across. Giant redwood trees can reach heights of 110 metres.

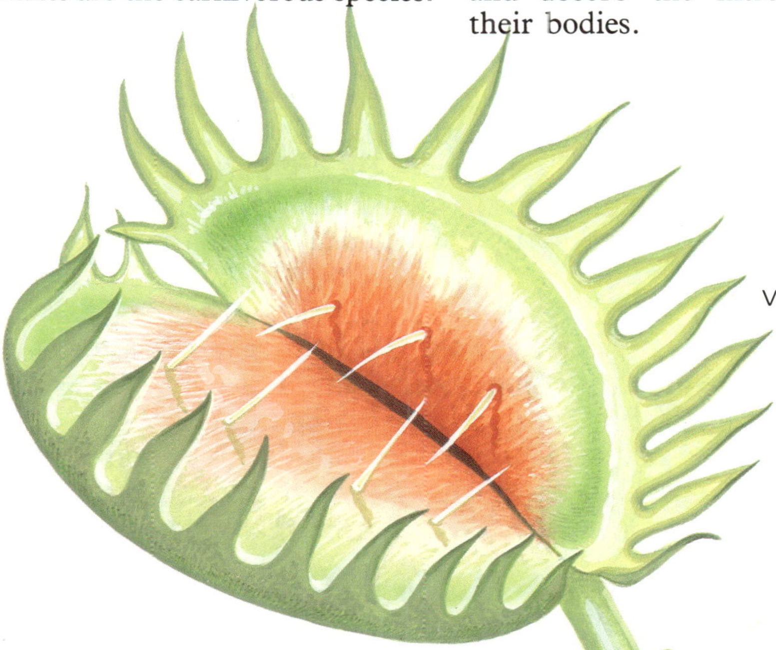

Venus fly trap

Carnivorous plants like the Venus fly trap and the pitcher plant eat small insects and other creatures.

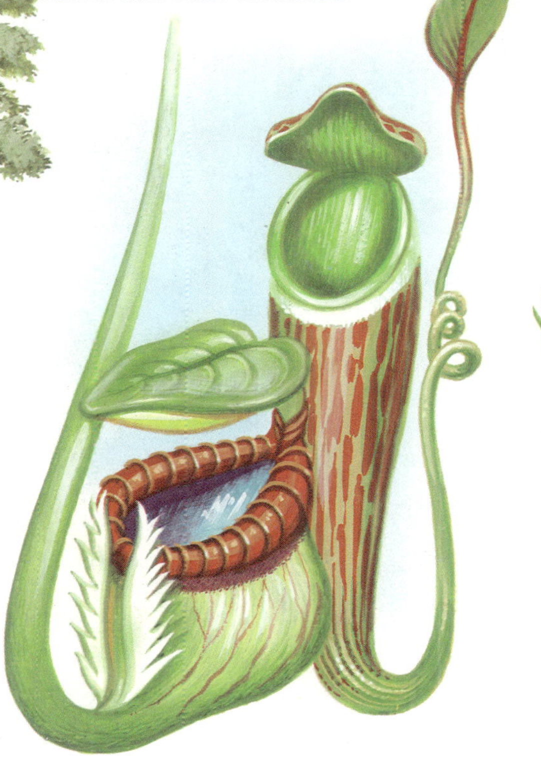

Pitcher plant

The Animal Kingdom

The Animal Kingdom can be divided simply into two large groups: animals without backbones (also known as invertebrates) and animals with backbones (also known as vertebrates).

Some of the more familiar invertebrate animals we see around us include insects, crabs, worms and spiders. Animals like cats and dogs, snakes, frogs, birds and fishes belong to the other group, the vertebrates.

Vertebrate animals are generally much bigger than invertebrate animals. They also *seem* to be more common. However, there are many more invertebrate animals in the world than there are vertebrate animals. About 95 per cent of the whole Animal Kingdom is composed of invertebrate animals. Many of them spend much of their lives hidden from view, however — in the soil, in the sea or concealed among the bark of trees.

Animal Classification

Animals (and plants) are grouped together according to particular features that they have in common. We have already seen how animals can be grouped into vertebrates and invertebrates. The next major division within the Animal Kingdom is the phylum. Animals within a phylum also share many features in common. For instance, the animals grouped together in the Phylum Arthropoda all have a tough, external skeleton called an exoskeleton, and jointed legs.

Within each phylum the animals are arranged in separate classes. Animals within each class share many common features of body structure. Thus, within the Phylum Arthropoda, the Class Insecta includes all those animals whose bodies are divided into three parts and bear three pairs of legs — in other words, the insects.

The next division, within the classes, is the order. Within each order are usually a number of families. Families contain animals which are similar in many ways. In the world of birds, all the tits (blue tit, coal tit and so on) are grouped together in the same family.

The next division is the genus. The final division is the species. All the species within a particular genus are basically alike. It is only animals of the same species breeding together which can produce young animals capable of themselves breeding.

Right: This family tree of the Animal Kingdom shows the main groups of animals which have appeared on earth.

Left: Although they all look quite different, all these animals are mammals. Their bodies bear fur and they suckle their young.

Crustaceans
Segmented worms
Flatworms
Echinoderms
Fishes
Birds
Molluscs
Roundworms
Insects
Reptiles
Mammals
Amphibians
Arachnids
Protochordates
Sponges
Bryozoans
Protozoa
Comb jellies
Jellyfishes

Animals of Australia

Australia is a huge continent in the South Pacific. Together with other islands such as New Zealand and New Guinea, it forms an area called Australasia. Naturalists have always been fascinated by the wildlife of Australia, for many of the animals there are found nowhere else in the world today.

Many millions of years ago the land masses of the Australasian region were connected to the rest of the world. All the animals roamed freely across the continents because at that time they were not separated by great oceans.

Then, the continents began to drift apart. Australia and the other countries of Australasia slowly moved towards the South Pole. Now, all the kinds of animals which were living there became separated, or isolated, from all the other countries of the world by thousands of kilometres of ocean.

Before the drift began most of the mammals were of the kind called marsupials. They had pouches in which the young developed. There were also some other, even stranger, mammals called monotremes. They laid eggs. Cut off from the rest of the world, Australia's mammals developed into many species quite different from the mammals which later arose in other parts of the world.

Above: Some of Australia's birdlife is also very unusual. The kookaburra is related to the kingfishers. It has a very distinctive call and because of this is also known as the 'laughing jackass'. Some Australian birds, such as the bee-eater, birds of Paradise, parrots and cockatoos, are beautiful birds with extremely colourful plumage. Birds of Paradise and parrots live in dense forests, but bee-eaters prefer sandy banks and kookaburras live near water.

INTRODUCED MAMMALS

The arrival of the first men in Australia several thousand years ago caused some important changes. The earliest men brought with them domestic dogs. Some of these returned to the wild and began to prey on the marsupial mammals, which were unable to defend themselves. The later settlers brought sheep and cattle. The farmers who tended these animals drove many of the native animals off their grazing land. Other introduced mammals such as rats and rabbits also competed with the marsupials for food and territory. Today, many marsupials are in danger of extinction, and special measures have been taken to protect them.

The platypus is one of only two mammals in the world which lay eggs. The other egg-laying mammal is the echidna, or spiny anteater. Both of these mammals are known as monotremes. Although these mammals lay eggs, they still feed their young on milk just as other mammals do. Monotremes also have a beak, instead of teeth, and the males have a poisonous claw on their hind legs. The platypus lives in burrows in river banks. It spends most of its life in the water, where it swims about searching for small creatures to eat.

Right: This scene shows some more Australian animals. Many of Australia's animals live in the hot dry interior of the country known as the outback. The frilled lizard raises the frill around its neck in order to frighten would-be predators, although the animal is in fact harmless. Note the young kangaroos, known as joeys, which are carried in their mothers' pouches. Flocks of budgerigars roam across Australia, feeding on seeds. In some places they are considered pests, as they feed on crops. In the forests of eastern Australia the koala is to be found. This mammal looks like a small bear with tufted ears. It feeds on eucalyptus leaves and is only active at night. The emu is a large, flightless bird. Although it cannot fly, it can run extremely fast to escape from its enemies.

Life on the African Plains

Below: A cheetah chases after a group of impala, scattering giraffes and ostriches as it does so. Although very young elephants might fall victim to predatory cats, the cheetah would not dare attack with a protective adult elephant close by.

The African Plains are vast belts of grassland stretching across the continent. Some of the African Plains occur in the temperate regions of southern Africa, but most are found in the tropics. Rainfall occurs for only a short period in tropical grasslands. When it rains the grass grows high and lush. Between the rains the land looks rather barren, with few trees.

The grasses provide food for a variety of large animals such as elephants, giraffes, deer and zebra. Smaller animals like insects and snakes find shelter and food among the grasses, too.

Life on the African Plains can be harsh. The grazing animals must constantly be on the lookout for predators, and they may struggle to survive in years when droughts occur. During droughts, the grasses shrivel and die, fires are common, and even waterholes may dry up. Then, the great herds of grazing animals must often roam far in search of water and food.

Animals of the African Plains

One of the most astonishing sights in nature is to see the huge herds of animals such as wildebeest, many thousands of individuals strong, as they move slowly across the plains. Sometimes herds of different animals such as zebras and antelopes will join together for mutual protection, the whole herd alert to danger.

Few of the grazing animals compete with each other for food, for each type specializes in eating different vegetation. The tall acacia trees can only be reached by giraffes, smaller bushes are eaten by other grazers like eland, and the grasses are eaten by rhinoceroses, zebras and gazelles.

The birdlife of the African Plains includes the huge, flightless ostrich as well as birds of prey like the secretary bird, which attacks and eats snakes. Hidden among the vegetation are hordes of insects, spiders and other small creatures. These provide food for small rodents and reptiles, which themselves may fall prey to other predators.

Predators

The many herds of grazing animals provide food for the carnivorous animals of the African

Plains. The best known of these are the cats—the lions, cheetahs and leopards. Antelopes and zebras form the main food for the cats. Each of the cats has its own special way of catching food. Lions normally hunt in groups. They may lie in wait at a waterhole or surprise a herd on the open plain. Often some of the lions in the group will chase prey to where other lions are waiting.

Cheetahs rely on their great speed to catch prey. They will wait silently, crouched among the grass, until they single out a victim from the herd. Then they bound after their prey at great speed. Cheetahs can run at over 100 kilometres per hour for short distances, but they soon become exhausted and give up the chase if they have not caught their prey within about 40 metres. Leopards eat small antelopes and birds.

Once the prey is brought down and killed with a bite to the neck, it is dragged to safety and eaten. Members of a pride of lions will often feed on the prey together, the strongest individuals taking the best pieces. When the cats have had their fill, it is time for other creatures of the plains to join the feast. First to arrive will often be the hyaenas, which scrap noisily between each other over the left-overs. Then come the vultures, and finally the scavenging insects.

In the Amazon Jungle

The Amazon Jungle is part of a huge rain forest covering much of tropical South America. Rain forests are special kinds of forest. Here, the temperature is high all year round and heavy rainfall occurs frequently. These conditions are just right for rich plant growth, and within rain forests we find many kinds of luxuriant trees and other plants such as orchids, ferns and bromeliads.

LIFE IN THE JUNGLE CANOPY

Although some animals are to be found living on the floor of the rain forest, many more creatures live among the canopy. Brightly coloured birds like toucans and parrots fly among the treetops, and groups of monkeys live in noisy family groups. Here we also find the predatory animals such as snakes, and harpy eagles which swoop down to snatch birds and small monkeys in their sharp talons. Sometimes predatory cats such as jaguars also climb the trees in search of prey.

Right: The world's tropical rain forests are found in equatorial regions where the temperature is always above 18°C (65°F) and where at least 200 centimetres of rain falls each year. The world's rain forests are being destroyed as man clears them to make way for land to farm. Since 1945 over half of all the world's rain forests have been cut down.

The trees in rain forests consist of species like ebony, teak and mahogany. They grow close together, with their upper branches thrusting towards the sky. The top-most parts of the trees form a layer known as the canopy. The leaves of the canopy layer shade most of the sunlight due to their density, and so the forest floor is gloomy, with little plant growth. Most of the other plants of the rain forest grow on the trunks and stems of the trees, about 15 metres off the ground where some sunlight still penetrates. Plants which grow on other plants are called epiphytes.

Below: Seen from the air, the Amazon rain forest appears as a dense canopy of leaves. These upper branches are the home of many animals, such as monkeys, birds and snakes. On the floor, where little light penetrates, live creatures such as huge beetles and centipedes, as well as deer and the pig-like tapir. Jaguars move stealthily among the tree roots, waiting to pounce on their prey.

Streams and Ponds

Plants and animals in streams and ponds have a very different kind of life from those on the seashore. For one thing the water is fresh. For another, the water level, though it may change according to how much rain has fallen, is much more constant than on the seashore. The plants and animals are also much more closely linked to the land around them.

Some ponds are small and shallow, and their waters are more or less stagnant. Others are deep lakes. Some are constantly enriched by material that is washed into them from streams. Plants grow in shallow mud, especially around the edges of ponds. These water weeds provide shelter for such creatures as water snails, worms, freshwater shrimps and leeches. There are also many larvae of insects such as stoneflies, mayflies and caddis flies. In deeper water there are such creatures as water-fleas (daphnia) and the fishes that feed on them.

RIVER REACHES

Rivers can be classified according to how fast the water flows through them. The water is faster and more *turbulent* (churned up) in mountainous regions, and slower and more gentle in the flat plains. The speed of the water, plus its depth and temperature, affect the type of fish found in a particular reach. For example, trout like fast, cold mountain streams, whereas bream prefer deeper and warmer slow-running rivers.

From its source to its mouth, a river can be divided into four zones, each one named after the fish most commonly found there. They are the trout, minnow, chub and bream regions.

POND LIFE

However quiet a pond may look on the surface, it is a busy place under water. Frogs lay their eggs there, and the eggs hatch into wriggling, active tadpoles. The frogs' relatives, the newts, also lay their eggs in water, and the warty newts tend to stay there all the time.

The many fishes include sticklebacks. At breeding time the male stickleback builds a nest of bits of plant, in which the female lays her eggs.

Many nymphs, the young of certain insects, live in water, and so do some adults, though they have to come to the surface to breathe.

The great diving beetle, up to 40 mm long, attacks almost any living thing in the pond, including small fishes.

Water birds include ducks, swans and coots, which feed on fish and insects. The commonest duck is the mallard, which nests on shore.

Below: A panorama of the rich and varied life to be found in and close to a river, from its source in the mountains to the time it flows into the sea. The stonefly and the mayfly are two insects well known to fishermen, because they are popular food for the brown trout, which gives its name to this stretch of the river. The insects' larvae are eaten by such fish as the miller's thumb, also called the bullhead. In the same region is the dipper, a bird that stands on the stream bed watching for food, mostly insects.

In the next stretch the minnow and grayling are common fishes. The minnow is a popular food for the brightly-coloured kingfisher.

Roach are found when the stream is flowing at a moderate pace. They also feed on insect larvae, such as the young of dragonflies, and on various plants. Moorhens nest on the banks. Nearer the sea, perch are abundant, and in the river mouth such sea fishes as flounder and mullet live. Herons fish in the shallows.

Some of the wild flowers to be found in or near streams are shown along the bottom of the picture. The sea aster is a coastal plant.

Life in the Mojave Desert

Deserts are found in parts of the world where there is very little rainfall. Most deserts are hot, dry places but some are very cold. On average, less than 25 centimetres of rain falls each year in deserts. Sometimes it may not rain in the desert at all for several years. Then torrential rain will fall, bringing floods which sweep through the desert.

Deserts are usually rocky or sandy, with little vegetation. The plants and animals which live in deserts have to find special ways of living in the harsh, dry conditions.

The Mojave Desert is in southern California, in the U.S.A. It covers an area of about 38,850 square kilometres.

Animals of the Mojave Desert

As in other hot deserts, animals of the Mojave Desert have developed special methods to help them keep cool and conserve water. Many animals burrow underground by day. In the Mojave Desert the temperature may be 35°C lower underground than on the surface by day. At night, when the temperature has dropped, the animals leave their burrows to hunt for food.

Animals such as desert rats have large eyes which help them to see at night. Hunters such as snakes rely on sensing the warm bodies of their prey in order to track them down.

When desert animals must travel about during the daytime, they move very fast so that they do not remain too long in contact with the hot ground. The roadrunner uses its great speed to catch lizards and small snakes.

Plants of the Mojave Desert

The largest and most spectacular plants of the Mojave Desert are the cacti. Saguaro cacti can grow to over 16 metres in height. Cacti absorb water very quickly when it rains and then store it in their thick leaves and stems. Plants which can do this are called succulents. The creosote bush is another strange desert plant which can actually survive being dried up by the sun's rays.

When the rains come, all the desert plants quickly bloom, and seeds which had lain dormant in the ground suddenly germinate. For a short while the barren desert becomes a flower-filled landscape.

Above: The desert is full of animal life, although most species spend the day hiding away in the shade. The map at the top shows the main deserts of the world.

Ends of the Earth

The polar regions cover the most northern and most southern areas of the globe. In the northern hemisphere the polar region is called the arctic, and in the southern hemisphere it is called the antarctic. Animals that live in the polar regions have to endure some of the harshest conditions on earth. There are permanent snow and ice fields over much of the areas, and there is always the chance of a sudden icy blizzard, even in summer.

Rich Life in the Seas

Most of the land in the polar regions is either covered with snow, or is frozen just below the surface. As a result, few animals can find food here.

However, the polar seas are extremely rich in food, and provide food for birds such as penguins, and mammals such as bears, whales and seals.

Long Days and Nights

In the polar regions, the sun never climbs very high in the sky, even at the height of summer. As a result, its warming effect is never properly felt. However, throughout the summer it never sets, giving the polar inhabitants perpetual daylight.

In the winter, however, the sun only rises above the horizon each day for a few hours at most. At the poles themselves it does not rise at all for several weeks. Many of the animals move away from the poles in winter to find milder climates and more daylight.

Top left: Some animals stay and endure the arctic winter. A few, like the ptarmigan, turn white to camouflage them against the snow.

Left: In the summer, the arctic tundra is visited by many migrant birds such as waders and geese. The ptarmigan and arctic fox lose their white coloration.

Below: The dramatic antarctic is home to millions of penguins.

Birds Around the World

Birds are found all around the world, from the hottest deserts to the icy polar caps. Some are specialized and have restricted distributions. Thus, secretary birds are found only on the African Plains, and hummingbirds are found only in the Americas. Other species have wider distributions. The golden eagle, for instance, is found all over the northern hemisphere.

Birds are grouped into families which share recognizable features. Some families have representatives in all parts of the world. For example, ducks, geese and swans can be found in almost every habitat, and all share a similar appearance with webbed feet and a flattened bill. Puffins, and their relatives the auks, on the other hand, are only found in the northern hemisphere.

Nectar Eaters

Hummingbirds are a very specialized group of birds which can hover while collecting nectar from flowers. They are usually very colourful birds with iridescent plumage. Hummingbirds are only found in the Americas, with most species occurring in Central and South America.

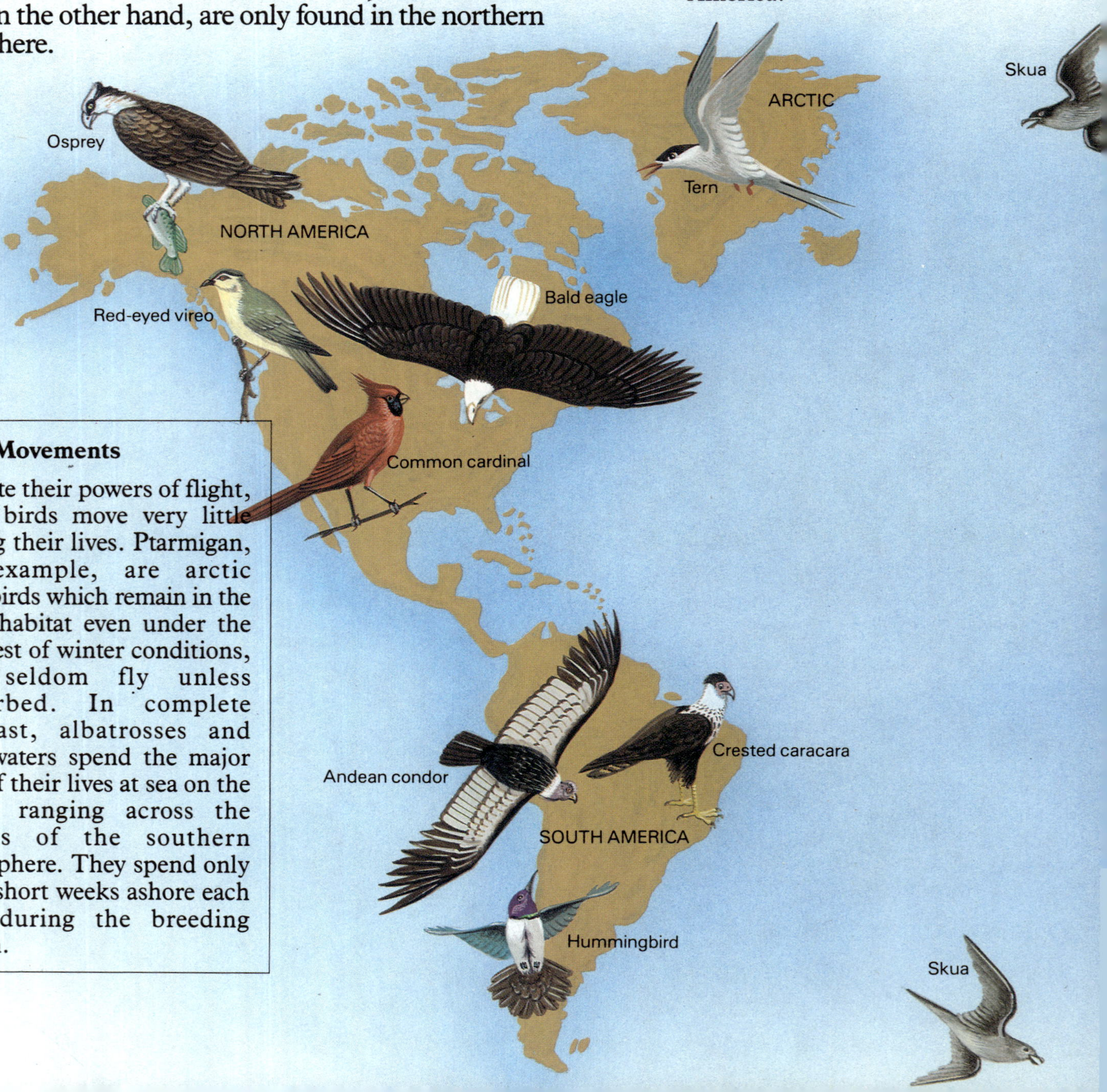

Bird Movements

Despite their powers of flight, some birds move very little during their lives. Ptarmigan, for example, are arctic gamebirds which remain in the same habitat even under the harshest of winter conditions, and seldom fly unless disturbed. In complete contrast, albatrosses and shearwaters spend the major part of their lives at sea on the wing, ranging across the oceans of the southern hemisphere. They spend only a few short weeks ashore each year during the breeding season.

In Africa, the sunbirds have also evolved to collect nectar. They cannot hover and are not related to hummingbirds, but look remarkably similar at first glance.

Birds of Prey

Birds of prey are found all over the world. They have sharp talons which they use to grip their prey, and a hooked beak to tear the flesh. They range in size from the tiny pygmy falcon, no bigger than a sparrow, to immense eagles which can soar effortlessly for hours on end.

Some birds of prey are specialized to feed on carrion. These are the vultures and the condors. They are not very closely related, although they look similar. Condors are found only in the Americas whereas vultures only occur in Europe, Africa and Asia.

Birds of the Antarctic

The most characteristic birds of the antarctic are the penguins. These rather comical birds feed on the abundant marine life in the polar seas.

There are many different species but they all share the same characteristics. They have lost the ability to fly. Instead, they use their wings as flippers to swim, almost like flying, under water. Their feathers form a dense, insulating layer against the freezing waters and biting wind. They are an extremely successful family, and colonies often number over a million birds.

Below: Birds are found on all continents of the world.

Friends and Foes

Above: The speedy cheetah makes a dash to catch an antelope. But if the antelope can keep running the cheetah soon tires and gives up the chase.

Above: The pangolin, or scaly anteater, rolls itself into a ball when danger threatens.

Animals in the wild have few friends, and many enemies. On land, the grazing animals, such as deer, antelopes, elephants and bison form large herds. A herd itself is a protection against danger, but often the stronger animals deliberately guard the weaker; for example, when musk oxen form their protective circle they place the younger animals in the centre.

In the sea, fish often stay together in huge shoals, and so do many species of whales. Whales and dolphins have been seen supporting and escorting an injured companion.

Animal Partners

Some of the most remarkable 'friendships' are those between animals of different species. They live together for mutual support, a state known as *symbiosis*. The hermit crab lives in a discarded shell, and has a sea anemone on the outside of the shell. The stinging cells of the sea anemone

Below: The Australian frilled lizard tries to frighten away its attackers by hissing and spreading out a fold of skin.

protect the crab, and the anemone benefits from food particles discarded by the crab. When the crab grows and moves to a bigger shell, it takes its sea anemone with it.

Little fishes known as wrasses living in the Indian and Pacific oceans act as cleaners for bigger fish. They eat parasites, such as fish-lice, on the bodies of the larger fish, which queue up to be cleaned.

When Danger Threatens

Danger in the wild comes from the *carnivores*, the flesh-eaters, who prey on the *herbivores*, the plant-eaters. The term 'carnivore' includes not only such large animals as tigers and hyenas, but also many birds which prey on small creatures such as insects.

Some animals, such as the springbok, rely on their speed to escape from danger. The hedgehog curls up, presenting a predator with an unappetising ball of prickles. Many animals have *protective coloration*: their colouring matches that of their background. For example, a white Arctic hare is hard to see against snow. Small creatures often look like something else: there are moths which resemble bird droppings, insects which look like leaves or twigs, and plaice which match the sea bed on which they lie. Many creatures, such as wasps, are harmful to eat, and have *warning coloration*, generally red or yellow and black. Other animals mimic this coloration, even though they are not unpleasant to eat; for example, hoverflies look very like wasps.

Above: Some examples of insect camouflage on a tree trunk. At the top a katydid nestles among leaves of a similar colour. The stick insect poses to look just like a twig on the side of the tree, while the treble bar moth has colouring like the trunk itself. The leaf-insect 'hides' by sitting openly on a leaf. Even bright colours can be a camouflage, as can be seen in the yellow crab spider crouched on a buttercup awaiting its prey.

Right: Oxpeckers are African starlings which spend their lives living on large animals, such as the Cape buffalo shown here. They feed on ticks and other parasites which they pull out of the animals' skin. They warn their hosts when danger is about by uttering loud cries and flying about in the air. The large animals take no notice of their companions except when they give the alarm. The birds make their nests in holes in trees, or in rocks.

Nature Trails

The best way to find out about animals and plants is to take a walk in the country, or even take a look in a town garden.

Many national parks and country parks have nature trails marked out to lead naturalists to the places where they can see the most interesting plants and animals. They often provide identification plates similar to those opposite, to help people to put a name to what they see.

Most naturalists following nature trails find that it is a good plan to take a notebook and pencil, to make a record of anything they see, and even a sketch to help identification later. Binoculars are a great help for studying birds, and a pocket magnifying glass is essential to find out the details of plants which may look alike to the casual eye.

There is another form of nature trail, too – that left by the feet of animals as they go about their daily lives. Such footprints show up best in snow, but they can also be detected in soft ground, and even in dewy grass. There are other marks, too, that betray the presence of animals, such as the claw marks which badgers leave on the trees and logs they use as scratching posts, or holes in a bank which are home to some small creatures.

The best time to see and identify tracks left by animals is when snow is on the ground. Remember animals leave slightly different marks according to the way they are moving, and this shows up clearly in snow.

Oak
Lombardy poplar
Birch
Scots pine
Larch
Poppy
Meadow thistle
Lesser celandine
Common violet
Cuckoo-pint
Tawny owl
Swallow
Redstart
Lapwing
Pochard
Mouse, bounding
Rabbit, hopping slowly
Stoat, bounding
Squirrel, jumping

Nature in the Garden

It is not always necessary to go on a nature trip to the countryside, or to the seashore, in order to find plenty of wildlife. For many of our own back gardens provide a wonderful haven for plants and animals.

Some gardens are better than others for attracting wildlife. The best ones are those with plenty of trees growing in them, and where a part of the garden is allowed to grow 'wild'. This can easily be done by sowing some wild flower seeds in a small corner, or allowing a little of the lawn to grow longer than usual.

A pond will also prove to be a welcome feature for wild animals, many of which will come to drink, feed or lay their eggs. A small pile of rocks of even just a few bricks will make a home for spiders, slow worms and other small creatures.

However, even if your garden is a neat, tidy place without any trees, there will always be some wildlife present. All gardens

have soil, of course, and this is where many of the smaller creatures of the garden live. Earthworms are the gardener's friend, for they help mix the earth together, and create air passages for the roots of plants. Other animals of the soil include beetles and their larvae, centipedes and millipedes, and ants. If you carefully lift a large stone in the garden you will often see ants scuttling about, for they often build their nests under stones.

Sometimes gardeners find large heaps of soil on their carefully tended lawns. These are caused by moles, which burrow through the earth and push the soil they have excavated up on to the grass.

Hidden among the fallen leaves or creeping between the stems of the flowers in the flower beds are other animals such as slugs and snails.

Many of the creatures of the garden are very secretive. They remain hidden from view and only emerge from the safety of their hiding places to feed at night. Birds, however, are among the easiest of garden animals to see. We can encourage them by planting trees, or by growing bushes with berries which they can eat in the autumn. In winter, a bird feeding table will also attract hungry flocks, eager for something to eat.

Wild plants, too, will find their way into the garden. The plants we call weeds are really just wild flowers growing uninvited. In autumn, mushrooms and toadstools will appear mysteriously from the ground, and lichens, mosses and other lowly plants will soon colonize rocks.

Above: You can easily make a wormery yourself. The one shown here is made from two sheets of glass with soil sandwiched between them, but a jam jar containing some moist soil and a few leaves is just as good. Watch the earthworms mix the soil as they burrow through it.

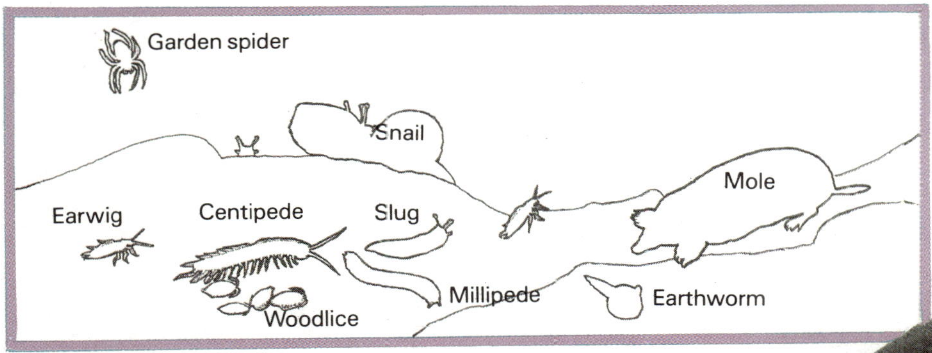

Below: Some common garden animals. Many of the smaller creatures spend the day hidden under stones or leaves, but at night they are much more active and can easily be seen with the aid of a torch.

Index

Illustrators
Mike Atkinson, Jim Dugdale, Ron Jobson, Linden Artists Ltd.,
John Marshall, Bernard Robinson, Frederick St. Ward,
Mike Saunders and David Wright.

Cover illustrations by
Graham Austin/Garden Studio

 Published in
Great Britain by Cliveden Press,
an Egmont Company, Egmont House,
PO Box 111, Great Ducie Street,
Manchester M60 3BL.

Printed in Singapore.

ISBN 0 7498 0395 9

Reprinted 1992

THE WORLD OF
Animals

THE WORLD OF

Animals

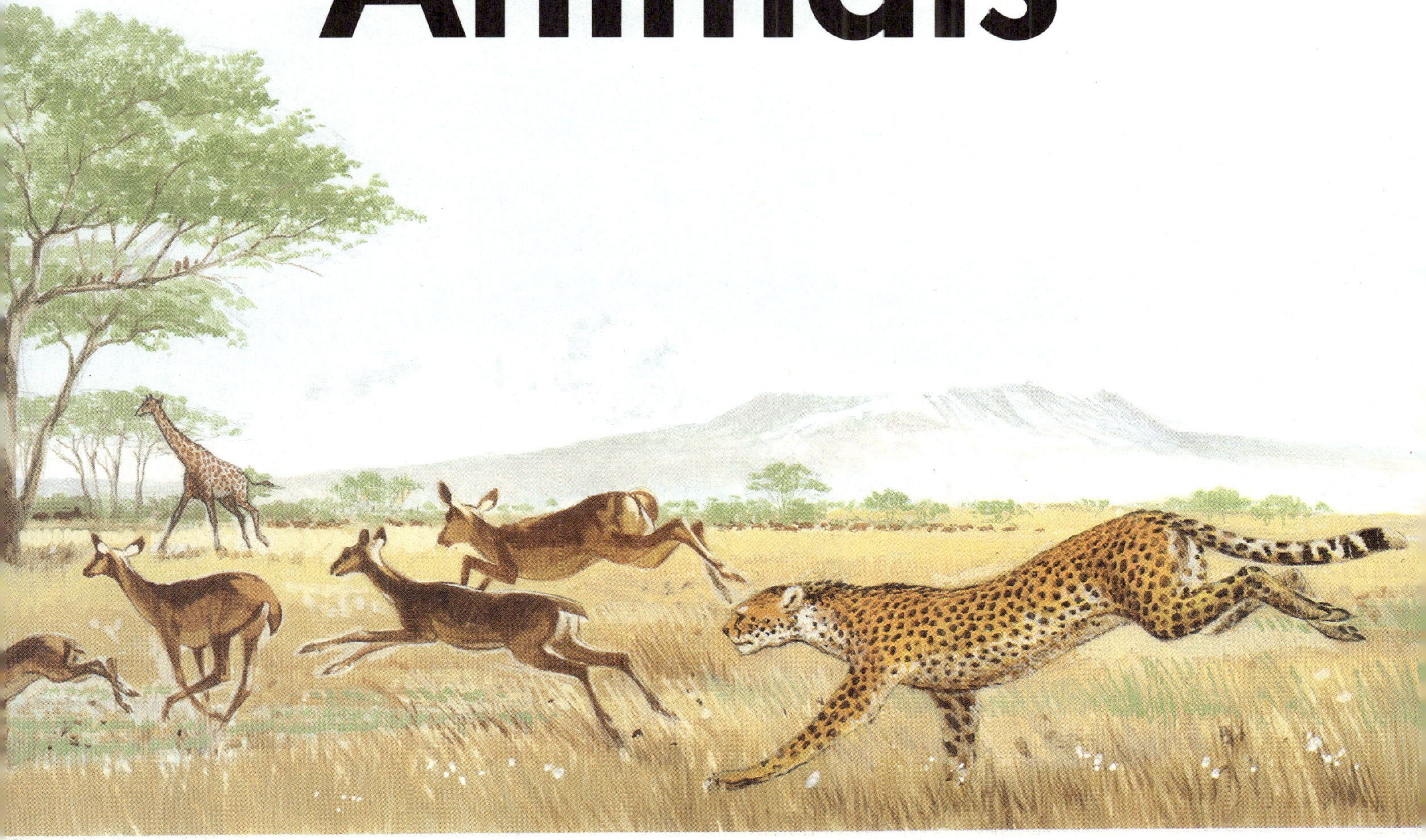

CLIVEDEN PRESS

Contents

Above: Charles Darwin was born in 1809, the son of a Shrewsbury doctor. Having abandoned careers in medicine and the church, he joined HMS *Beagle* as ship's naturalist. His voyages took him all round the world and helped inspire his theories of evolution.

Evolution in Action

Nowadays, evolution is an accepted fact, but it has not always been so. Once, people thought that life arose spontaneously from things like mud, water and air. The Biblical idea of creation was also widely accepted until scientists like Charles Darwin began to introduce new ideas.

Darwin's studies led him to believe that the present-day variety of life on earth had developed from much simpler creatures which lived long ago but had gradually died out, being replaced by more complex ones which were better suited to their environment. Only the most successful animals and plants survived and passed their characters on to their offspring. His ideas were criticized and ridiculed at the time, especially by the church, but he is now known to have been correct about many of his ideas concerning evolution.

Above: During his visit to the Galapagos, Darwin observed remarkable variation in the finches. On the widely separated islands there were separate races. Darwin suggested that all the races had evolved from the same original stock, a species from South America, and that each had adapted to the particular conditions on each island.

Below: Although no-one would confuse the adult forms of man, chicken and dogfish, it would take an expert to identify their embryos. Darwin suggested that the reason for their similarities was that they are all descended from a common ancestor and, during their development, they go through all the stages of evolution. All vertebrate embryos share many similar features as they develop, looking very much alike at some stages. At an early stage all embryos have gill pouches on their heads, a feature only retained in the adult form by fishes.

Studying Evolution

Of the countless millions of animals and plants which have lived and died on this earth before us, a small number died in places where their remains could be preserved as fossils until the present day. Some animals and plants lend themselves to fossilization because of their tough bodies. This is why there is an abundance of fossil pollen, and numerous species of shellfish. By examining changes in the fossil species and relating these to the geological time scale, we can begin to piece together the story of evolution – a process which still goes on today.

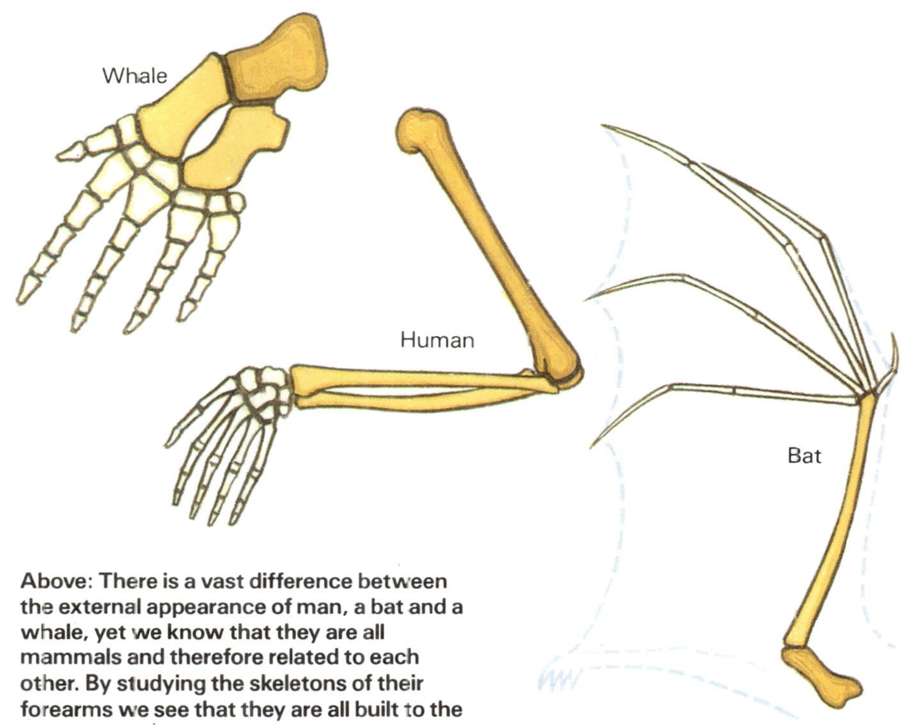

Above: There is a vast difference between the external appearance of man, a bat and a whale, yet we know that they are all mammals and therefore related to each other. By studying the skeletons of their forearms we see that they are all built to the same basic plan.

After travelling widely throughout the world and making detailed observations abroad and at home on domesticated animals, Darwin proposed that all life on earth had evolved gradually from the simplest forms over a vast period of geological time. As evidence for his theories he used fossil records, the 'artificial selection' of breeders of domestic pigeons, and his observations on adaptations of species on isolated islands.

In his book 'The Origin of Species', published in 1859, he explained his ideas about natural selection. Animals and plants produce a vast number of offspring in each generation, far more than are needed to maintain a stable population of the species. Most of the young die before they reach adulthood. Darwin proposed that only those most able to survive would do so, the rest would be 'selected out' by nature.

Animals of Long Ago

The first animals appeared on earth many millions of years ago. Their remains sometimes become preserved in rocks. When this happens the remains are known as fossils. By studying fossils, scientists have discovered almost everything they know about the animal life of long ago.

Life began in the oceans. The first forms of life were small, primitive creatures rather like the sponges and jellyfishes of today. In time, larger creatures such as crabs evolved. Then fishes appeared in the seas. Some of these fishes were huge, armour-plated monsters which preyed on other sea creatures.

Eventually fishes evolved which could breathe air. From them developed animals which were able to live both on land or in the water. These were the amphibians, the ancestors of the salamanders, frogs and toads. They first appeared about 350 million years ago.

Once the land had been conquered by animals, other creatures evolved. Next to arrive were the reptiles. For many millions of years, conditions on earth were exactly right for the reptiles, and they flourished in many parts of the world.

Right: *Pteranodon* was a huge flying reptile that lived during the Cretaceous Period, some 130 million years ago. It had a wingspan of about 7 metres. *Pteranodon* probably clambered up on to cliffs and launched itself into the air to soar and glide over the sea. *Pteranodon* had a long bony crest at the back of its head to help counter-balance the huge beak.

Far right: *Alamosaurus* lived in parts of Europe and North America during the Cretaceous Period. It was a large plant-eating dinosaur. *Tyrannosaurus* (the name means 'tyrant lizard') is shown here attacking *Alamosaurus*. *Tyrannosaurus* was the biggest carnivorous reptile ever to have lived. It stood over 6 metres tall.

Left: About one and a half million years ago, great ice sheets from the North Pole crept over many parts of the northern hemisphere. To keep warm, animals such as the woolly mammoth shown here grew long coats. Other shaggy coated animals included the woolly rhinoceros and the cave bear. The sabre-toothed tiger was one of several meat-eating animals which preyed on creatures at this time.

Pteranodon Alamosaurus Tyrannosaurus

The biggest reptiles were the dinosaurs. Dinosaurs ruled the earth for about 130 million years. Giant plant-eating reptiles wallowed in the swamplands, browsing on vegetation. On dry land herds of horned dinosaurs roamed about. Many of these plant-eating dinosaurs fell prey to ferocious carnivores like *Tyrannosaurus*.

Some reptiles took to the air, gliding about on leathery wings. Others returned to the sea to feed on fishes and other marine creatures. About 65 million years ago, however, most of the reptiles suddenly died out.

The Age of Mammals

By the time most of the reptiles had died out, the mammals and birds had already evolved. The mammals quickly filled all the habitats occupied by the reptiles. The first mammals were small, mouse-like animals. In time many other kinds of mammal also appeared. Some of these were plant-eaters and others became carnivorous, feeding on the plant-eaters. Today, the mammals are the dominant animals on earth.

Scientists have found fossil bones from many of these early mammals. We know that some were gigantic. There were ground sloths bigger than elephants, and a giant rhinoceros called *Baluchitherium* that was nearly as tall as a house.

Below: Some animals have become extinct in more recent times. The dodo, a bird about the size of a turkey, was once found on Mauritius island in the Indian Ocean. When sailors from visiting ships landed on the island they stole its eggs and killed the birds for food. The last dodo was killed little more than 200 years ago.

World Wildlife

About 200 million years ago, when dinosaurs roamed the Earth, the continents were joined together in a vast supercontinent called Pangaea. But slowly the continents drifted apart and animals living on one land mass became separated from those living on another. Each group of animals continued to change – to *evolve* – but, isolated from each other, they evolved in different ways. This is why, today, certain animals are found only on certain continents; why, for example, kangaroos are found only in Australia and llamas only in South America. The map shows animals typical of each area.

NORTH AMERICA

Only a narrow stretch of water separates North America from Asia. Often in the past the two land masses have been joined by a land bridge, and animals have been able to pass from one to the other. For this reason, many of the animals found in North America are closely related to those found in Asia and Europe.

SOUTH AMERICA

South America has many animals found nowhere else in the world. Some are quite strange in both appearance and behaviour, such as the sloth, spending its days hanging upside-down in the trees, or the toothless anteater, rummaging through ant hills with its long nose. There is also a wealth of beautiful birds such as the scarlet macaw in the tropical rain forests.

EUROPE AND ASIA

Many people live in Europe and Asia, and much of the land is farmed, so the larger wild animals are mostly confined to nature parks. But some animals, such as the fox, have adapted to living among people. Others, such as the giant panda, live only in the deepest parts of the forest.

AFRICA

The grasslands of Africa have the most varied collection of large grazing animals in the world – including the giraffe, elephant, rhinoceros, antelopes and many others. These animals and the carnivores which prey on them roam free in vast national parks.

AUSTRALASIA

Australia was the first continent to break away from Pangaea. It did so at a time when most of the world's mammals reared their young in pouches. These animals, called marsupials, flourished in Australia, but soon became extinct in other parts of the world. The koala and kangaroo are both marsupials, and are found only in Australia. The tuatara, a reptile found in New Zealand, is the nearest living relative of the great dinosaurs.

Animal Lives

There are well over one million different kinds of animals, and they live on almost every part of the Earth's surface. There is animal life in caves, in deserts, and in the deep oceans. Only the frozen wastes of Antarctica and the highest and bleakest mountains are without animals – and even then, a few insects and spiders manage to exist on the coast of Antarctica, while swifts have been seen flying not far from the top of the world's highest mountain, Everest.

Naming Animals

Animals are often grouped together according to their similarities. This is known as classification. For example, some animals live in water, some on land; some are meat-eaters, some eat plants, and some eat both. Zoologists, the people who study animals, classify them according to the structure of their bodies. The simplest scientific group is the *species*, animals that are basically alike and breed among themselves. Similar species are grouped in *genera* (singular *genus*), genera are grouped in *families*, families in *orders*, orders in *classes*, and classes in *phyla* (singular *phylum*). All the phyla together make up the animal kingdom. Every group, from species to phylum, has a Latin name. In this way zoologists can give a name to every different kind, even those which share the same common name: for example, there are 4,000 species called hoverflies!

Two types of metamorphosis. A butterfly (left) goes through four stages of development: egg, caterpillar, pupa, and adult. A frog's eggs (below) hatch first into limbless, long-tailed tadpoles. The tadpoles gradually grow legs and turn into frogs.

Top left: The cuckoo lays its egg in another bird's nest. The foster bird rears the cuckoo chick, which pushes the other chicks out of the nest.

Top centre: Some species of fish look after their eggs by carrying them around in their mouths until they hatch – and the very young fish also shelter in their mother's mouth.

Top right: When the weather is cold and food is scarce, animals such as the dormouse go into a deep, trance-like sleep, known as *hibernation*.

Left: Deer live in herds. They are usually peaceful animals, but during the rutting (mating) season the males fight each other for possession of the females, clashing their antlers together in fierce combat.

CHANGING SHAPE

Some animals go through a series of changes in shape before they become adults. This process is known as *metamorphosis*, from two Greek words meaning 'change of body'.

Butterflies and many other kinds of insects undergo a four-stage process. The insect starts life as an egg, and hatches into a larva (the larva of a butterfly is called a caterpillar). It spends a large part of its life as a larva, then shuts itself up in a case called a pupa, which it makes of silk. In the pupal stage the insect's body changes tremendously. Eventually it emerges as an adult.

Some insects, such as dragonflies, go through three stages: egg, nymph and adult. The nymph is similar to the adult and grows in size without changing shape.

Animals and Their Young

Wild animals have just two objectives in life: getting enough to eat, and finding a mate and breeding. Most animals move about for these purposes, though a few, such as corals, spend most of their lives fixed in one spot, filtering their food from the water in which they live.

All animals reproduce themselves. Some of the very simplest creatures, called protozoa, just divide to make two 'daughter cells'. Sponges throw out buds, which break off to form new individuals. But most animals reproduce sexually, by the mating of a male and a female. A female produces cells called eggs, and a male produces cells called sperm. When one of each kind of cell comes together they unite, and a new individual grows.

Many animals, including most fish and insects, never see their young. They lay and fertilize their eggs, and then leave them. Other animals look after their young until they are old enough to fend for themselves.

The World of Insects

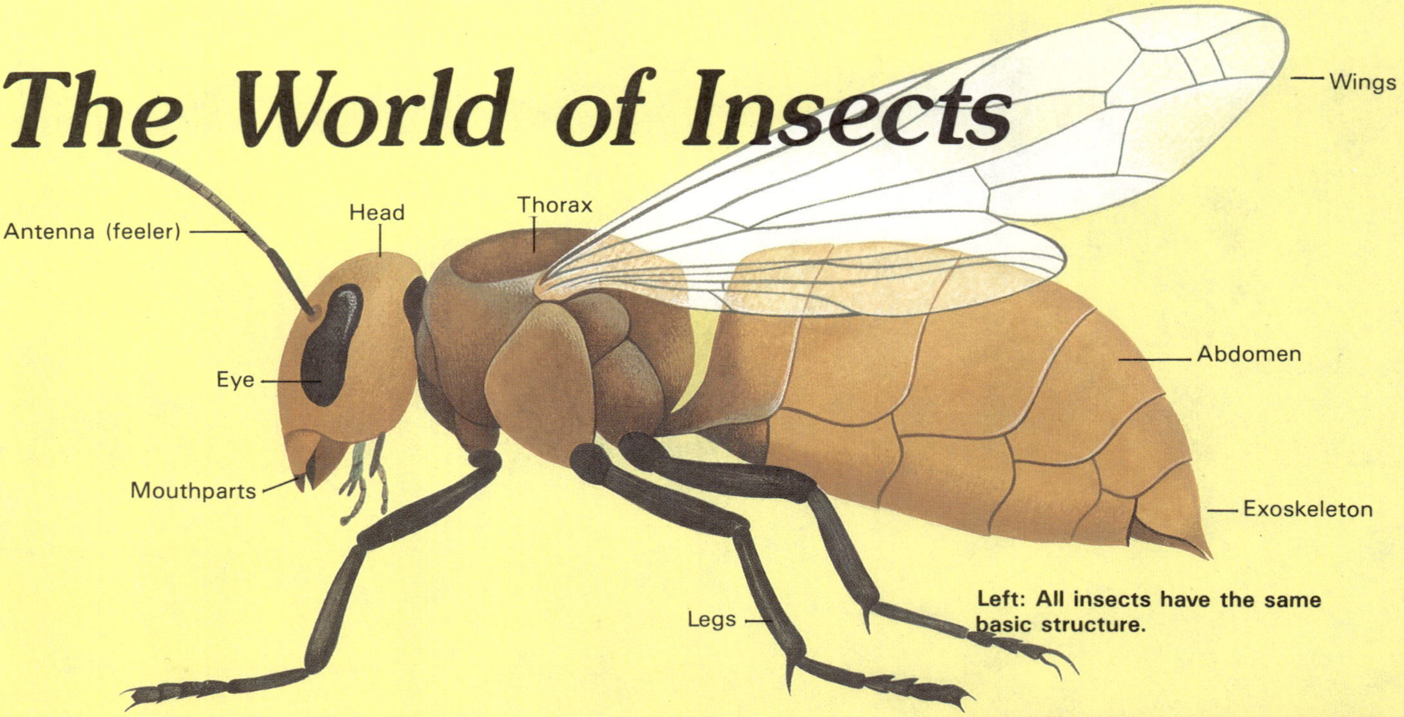

Left: All insects have the same basic structure.

Insects are the most numerous and widespread group of animals on earth. There are more species of insect than all the rest of the species in the Animal Kingdom put together. Over a million different kinds have been discovered. Insects are found in almost every sort of habitat, from deserts to lakes, and from the soil to the air. The only place which insects have been unable to colonize successfully is the oceans, but they make up for this by their abundance elsewhere. Insects vary enormously in their general shape as well as in their size. They range from the microscopic to beetles the size of a large mouse.

Despite the enormous variety of insect life, they all have certain features in common. Like many of their invertebrate relatives, insects have an external skeleton called an exoskeleton which provides support and protection. The bodies of adult insects are divided into three parts: the head, the thorax and the abdomen, and on the middle part are found three pairs of jointed legs.

Insect Lives

Perhaps the most striking feature of insects is their ability to fly. It is the conquest of the air which has helped insects to become so successful. Some insects, such as beetles, are relatively cumbersome in flight and can cover only short distances. Others, however, such as dragonflies, spend virtually all the hours of daylight on the wing. Their mastery of the air, and their excellent vision, allow them to catch even the speediest of airborne prey.

The wings of many butterflies are extremely colourful and are used for a variety of purposes such as display, defence and camouflage, in addition to their use in flight.

Insects eat many different types of food. Many, like the antlion larva above, are carnivores while others eat only plant material. Some insects even eat plants at one stage in their life and animals in another. Others are scavengers, or attack man's clothes, books and carpets. Even more extraordinarily some insects, such as certain moths, do not feed at all as adults.

Above: The antlion is a curious insect which is found in dry, sandy soils. The larva is a fierce carnivore with a liking for ants, but it is so slow and cumbersome that it has to use cunning means to catch its food. Instead of chasing its prey, the antlion larva buries itself in the sand and digs a pit. Any unfortunate ant which falls over the edge of the pit slowly but surely slides down into the jaws of the waiting larva.

Insects have well-developed senses that tell them everything they need to know about their surroundings. Unlike our own eyes, the 'compound' eyes of insects are composed of up to 25,000 separate chambers each with a small lens. Although giving

Here are some of the many different kinds of insects in the world. The vast array of insects can be subdivided into 29 main groups known as orders. Although all the members of these orders share the main features of insects, such as six true legs and a three-part body, in some species other features may be missing. For example, the parasitic insects such as fleas and lice have lost their wings. In the beetles the first pair of wings form a wingcase inside which the true wings are folded.

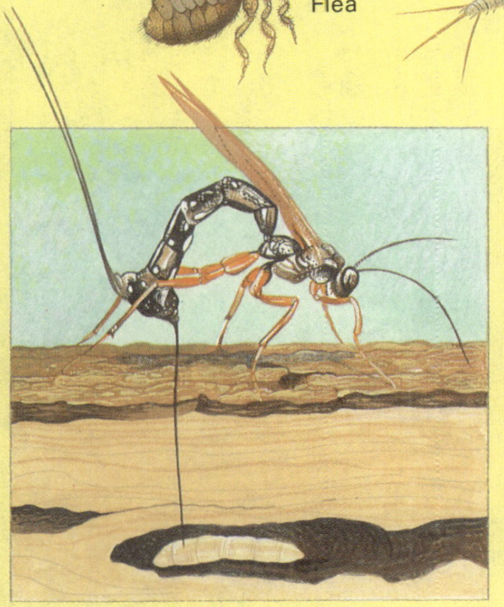

Above: Ichneumon wasps are fascinating insects which specialize in laying their eggs inside the bodies of other insect larvae. Since most insect larvae have soft skins this does not present many problems. But when the larva lives inside wood, difficulties can arise! Amazingly, some female ichneumon wasps can detect larvae buried up to several centimetres inside a tree. They then force a thin egg-laying tube, like a needle, through the wood to lay their eggs. When the ichneumon wasp eggs hatch, the young feed on the body of the larva.

Above: Insects have developed a variety of ways of ensuring that males and females find each other when they wish to mate. An especially ingenious method is used by glow worms. The female emits a strong glow at night which attracts not only our attention but also that of the male beetle.

Below: Many insects, such as the butterfly, have four very different stages in their life cycles. The adult butterfly lays eggs, from which hatch caterpillars. These are the feeding stage in the life cycle. The caterpillars turn into pupae by a process known as metamorphosis, and eventually the adult butterfly emerges, completing the life cycle. More primitive insects have a three-stage life cycle in which the eggs hatch directly into the nymphs, which are miniature versions of the adult.

less detail than our eyes, they give better all-round vision. Insects can also detect smells and temperature and pressure changes.

Social Insects

Above: Bees chew bark to make papery nests. These are sometimes built in crevices or suspended from branches. Workers collect pollen to make wax chambers for their young, and nectar to make honey.

Below: Some ants build large mounds of twigs and other plant material. These contain runs and galleries in which the ants live. Many species of ants have a special relationship with aphids. They collect honeydew from the aphids and in return protect them from predators.

Most insects lead independent lives, coming together with others of their kind only for mating. However, some insects can only survive in complex societies. On their own they would soon die.

In insect societies the whole colony is often based on one breeding female, called a queen. In most cases, all the other members of the society are her offspring. There is usually a well-defined division of labour, with different types of colony members produced for different tasks. This is called a caste system. For example, some members of the colony will defend it, and they have large, aggressive mouthparts. Others may be concerned with collection of food and repairing the nest or hive, and may have chewing mouthparts.

In the ants and termites, the solitary queen is often little more than an egg-laying machine. She devotes all her life to laying eggs but cannot defend or feed herself.

Ants

Ants are interesting social insects which live in large colonies either underground or in loose mounds. Their homes contain a complex system of tunnels and galleries. Ant societies contain three castes: the males, fertile females which become queens, and workers. In the summer, many ants produce wings and fly about looking for mates. These flights are called swarming flights. After mating the fertilized female sheds her wings and searches for a site to start a new colony.

Honey Bees

Honey bees are social insects which man uses to his advantage. In the wild, honey bees nest in cavities, but they take readily to artificial hives. Here their honey can be collected without harming the bees.

There are three castes in a honey bee society. At the centre of the colony is the large queen. She is fertile and lays eggs throughout her life, although she only mates once. The next caste is the drones. These are male bees. Their function is to mate with the queen, and they take no part in the running of the hive. The third caste is the workers, which make up most of the bees in the hive. Like the queen, they are female, but they are sterile. As their name suggests, they do most of the work, gathering pollen, making honey and defending the hive with their stings.

Honey bees show many interesting types of behaviour. In hot weather, they fan the entrance to the hive with their wings to produce a draught. The workers also perform elaborate 'dances' which tell other hive members the directions to the best food.

Termites

Termite mounds, like the ones shown at the bottom of this page, are a conspicuous feature of the African Plains, and are common throughout the tropics. These impressive structures may be up to 6 metres tall. Many are made of cemented soil and so they are virtually impregnable.

Termite society is rather different from those of ants, bees and wasps. There are four castes rather than three. A colony is started after winged males and females swarm. When a pair have settled, they shed their wings and the female becomes the queen of the new colony. She becomes grotesquely enlarged and lays more than 10,000 eggs a day when she is mature. The male is also important because he has to fertilize the queen several times throughout her life.

The soldiers are armed with a huge set of jaws with which to defend the mound from attackers. The fourth caste is the workers, who gather the wood which is the main food for termites. They have special bacteria in their intestines which help them digest it.

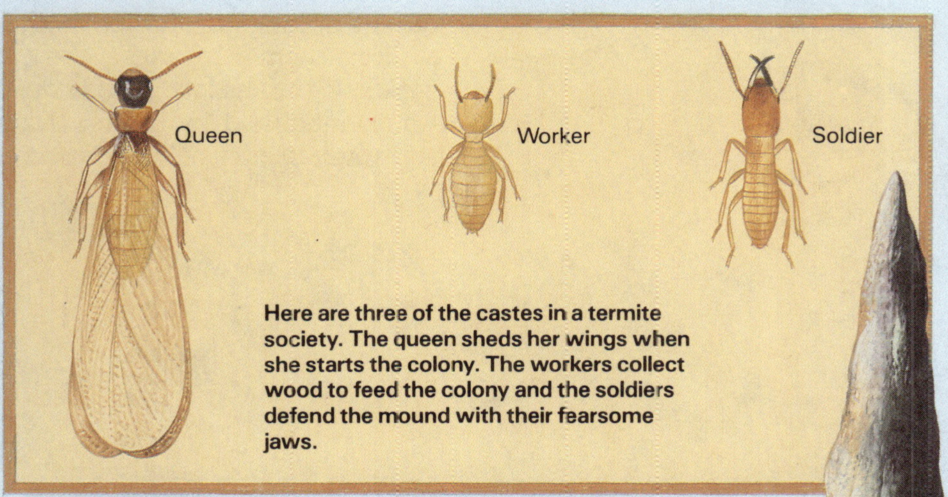

Here are three of the castes in a termite society. The queen sheds her wings when she starts the colony. The workers collect wood to feed the colony and the soldiers defend the mound with their fearsome jaws.

Below: The inset shows the swollen body of the mature termite queen. She grows to an enormous size and lays more than a million eggs in a year. She cannot feed or fend for herself and is looked after by the rest of the colony.

Pondlife

Freshwater ponds often teem with life. Colourful displays of flowers grow around their edges, and a wealth of animal life lives below the surface. The animals which dwell there must cope with very different problems from those of their relatives on land. They must be able to move about in the water and find a way of obtaining oxygen for breathing. The pond dwellers also have to cope with extremes of temperature; sunny days can heat the water up, while in winter the water's surface may freeze.

Some of the pond's inhabitants, such as fishes, can only live in water, but others, such as frogs and dragonflies, spend the early part of their lives in water and their adult stages on land, returning to the pond to breed in the spring.

Life in Ponds

The pond is not a simple environment, but is really a mixture of several separate habitats. The aquatic plants and animals have all evolved to live in very precise zones of the pond. Some plants will grow only in the drying mud on the margin of the pond while others, which cannot survive drying out, must be constantly immersed in water. Duckweed likes to drift in the open water while other species, such as water lilies, remain rooted in the mud at the bottom.

It is, however, the animal inhabitants which are most specially adapted to life in the pond. The surface of the water is very important. It is here that oxygen enters the pond from the air. It is the place where some animals move from air to water, and also where light penetrates the waters below. However, it can also be a prison to many land animals which get trapped in its surface film. Not surprisingly, a variety of scavengers live on the surface and pick off the unfortunate animals caught there. Still more scavengers live underneath this surface film, often trapping air on their bodies to keep them buoyant.

Below the surface is the open water, inhabited by newts, fishes and water beetles. These creatures

Right: This panorama of a pond illustrates some of the creatures which live there. In the water itself, great crested newts and sticklebacks feed on the wealth of insect life present. These in turn sometimes fall victim to the carnivorous great diving beetle. Beneath the surface of the water, many plants grow, rooted in the muddy bottom. When they flower, they either produce floating flowers, such as those of the water lily, or tall flowering spikes like those of reeds and bulrushes. Many birds are associated with fresh water. Herons patiently stalk fishes in the shallows while coots dive for plant and animal food.

feed on others which hide among the tangled pond weeds, and seldom visit either the surface or the bottom.

On the bottom, where the silt collects and where the remains of dead plants and animals fall, many species such as bloodworms and crustaceans tolerate its inhospitable conditions and find it a safe sanctuary away from the eyes of hungry predators.

In order to obtain the oxygen they require for breathing, many freshwater insects come to the surface to breathe, although some, such as damselfly nymphs, have developed simple gills to help them extract oxygen from the water. Many diving beetles have an ingenious way of breathing. They trap a bubble of air under their wingcases and this acts as a kind of 'aqualung'. But, like its human equivalent, it must be topped up from time to time, so the beetle makes regular visits to the surface.

Above: The development of tadpoles into frogs is a remarkable process. In early spring, frogs gather in large numbers in ponds to reproduce. The eggs are laid in great masses, and are surrounded by protective jelly which swells in the water producing the familiar 'frogspawn'. At first the little embryo is just a black dot, but it soon grows to form a tadpole and hatches after a couple of weeks. At this stage the tadpole breathes using feathery gills and rasps algae from the surface of pondweeds. Over the next few weeks it loses its external gills, develops legs and finally loses its tail. At this stage its metamorphosis is complete and the young froglet leaves the pond.

Water plants produce oxygen when they photosynthesize. One little animal named Hydra has found an ingenious way of making use of this. It incorporates small, single-celled green algae between its cells and then 'breathes' the oxygen they produce.

HALFWAY ANIMALS

Frogs, toads and newts belong to a group of animals known as amphibians. They are thought to have evolved from fish ancestors and to have given rise to reptiles. Fishes are almost exclusively aquatic animals, whereas reptiles are almost entirely land dwellers. Amphibians are usually just as much at home in water as they are on land.

When adults, frogs, toads and newts can breathe by taking in oxygen through their skins, but they can also gulp air through their mouths. This enables them to leave the water when they wish. Although some amphibians may spend most of their adult lives away from water, they must all return to the water to breed.

The Seashore

A great variety of interesting and unusual wildlife is to be found on the seashore. In fact, some of the plants and animals of the seashore — such as seaweeds and sea urchins — are found nowhere else.

All the animals and plants of the seashore are extremely hardy, for as well as having to cope with the pounding of the waves they must be able to survive when the tide goes out, leaving them exposed to the drying sun and wind. At this time they are also easy prey for predators, and so must find ways of protecting themselves.

The most common plants of the seashore are seaweeds. Seaweeds belong to a group of plants called algae. The seaweeds grow on the beach according to their ability to withstand exposure when the tide is out.

The most curious seashore plants are the lichens. Some resemble patches of tar stuck to the rocks. Others look like little orange crusty patches.

Types of Seashore

There are several different kinds of seashore. Rocky shores are usually richest in wildlife. The rocks provide good anchorage for the seaweeds, and the crevices offer a safe haven for snails, worms, crabs and other creatures. Many of the snails' relatives, such as limpets and mussels, clamp themselves to the rocks. Countless barnacles, related to crabs and prawns, also cover many of the rocks.

In the rockpools starfishes, anemones and fishes lurk, safe from the wind and sun.

Sandy shores are more difficult places for wildlife to survive. There is little shelter for animals, and so they must burrow beneath the sand to find a moist, secure place to live. Lugworms, fanworms and a great variety of bivalves such as cockles, razorshells and tellins are to be found living in the sand.

Even more harsh environments are shingle beaches. The relentless, grinding action of the pebbles would crush most animals. Therefore the only living things here are specially adapted flowering plants like sea kale.

Above: You will often find shells such as these on beaches. These shells once belonged to animals called molluscs, one of the commonest groups of creatures on the seashore. Other common molluscs include periwinkles and limpets.

Below: Seashores, particularly sheltered rocky shores, teem with animal and plant life. Some creatures live attached to the rocks themselves, while others seek refuge in rockpools or under the sand. Birds such as gulls and waders patrol the shore, looking for food.

ADAPTING TO LIFE ON THE SEASHORE

Some of the seashore animals have strong shells into which they can retreat at low tide, remaining moist and secure until the tide returns. Others are masters of camouflage; certain crabs and worms look like the seaweed in which they hide. The fronds of the seaweed also help to keep the creatures moist.

The seaweeds attach themselves to rocks by means of a root-like structure called a holdfast. They also have soft, slippery stems and fronds which enable them to sway in the currents and avoid becoming damaged. Some species, like bladderwrack, have special air bubbles in their fronds, which help them to float.

Life in the Seas

The seas and oceans cover nearly three-quarters of the world's surface, and are extremely rich and varied habitats. From the shallowest coastal waters to the huge expanses of the open ocean, and from the icy polar waters to the tropical seas, they literally teem with life.

Shallow Seas

In the shallow coastal waters we often find plants and animals similar to those found on the seashore, such as seaweeds, crabs, snails, bivalves (molluscs with hinged shells), starfishes and many other familiar creatures such as seals and sea lions.

In the warmer parts of the world the shallow waters are often the home of corals. These tiny creatures, related to anemones, build chalky homes around themselves. Eventually these may extend for many kilometres. Coral reefs are fascinating places in which fishes, starfishes, sea urchins and anemones and other creatures all live together in a bewildering array of colours and shapes.

Above: These dazzling clown fish are among the many colourful species which inhabit coral reefs. The world's biggest coral reef is the Great Barrier Reef, extending for 2012 kilometres along the north-eastern coast of Australia.

Below: Most sharks are fearsome predators of the sea, although a few species eat only plankton. Dolphins and porpoises are kinds of whale. Whales are mammals which spend all their lives in the sea. Many seabirds feed on fishes which they catch near the surface.

Open Oceans

The smallest forms of life in the open sea are the plankton. These are tiny, microscopic plants and animals which float near the surface. They provide food for many of the other species of animal living in the sea. Even some of the huge whales and sharks live just on a diet of plankton. Most of the sharks, however, are fierce predators of other animals, particularly the huge shoals of fishes which roam the oceans. Species such as the hammerhead and the great white shark are even feared by man, for attacks on humans are not uncommon in waters in which they are found.

Turtles and sea snakes are reptiles frequently encountered in the open sea. Turtles are generally found in warmer waters. They spend most of their lives at sea, only hauling themselves on to beaches at night to lay their eggs in the sand. As soon as they hatch, the baby turtles must scuttle back down the beach to return to the safety of the sea.

Sea snakes are highly venomous, and about 50 species are known to inhabit the sea, mainly in the waters of the Indo-Pacific region. They feed on small fishes.

Above: Jellyfishes and the Portuguese man o'war drift in the open oceans. They catch fishes and other small creatures, using their trailing tentacles which are armed with powerful stinging cells.

Deep Sea

In the gloom of the deep sea, where light never reaches, some of the most bizarre creatures are to be found. These include giant squids, prawns and angler fishes.

Below: The deep seas of the world are inhabited by species like the ones shown here. Many deep-sea creatures have special light-producing organs on their bodies to attract small prey.

The Reptilian World

Reptiles are scaly, cold-blooded vertebrate animals which lay eggs with hard, protective shells. The reptiles descended from amphibians 300 million years ago. Today, reptiles are found mainly in the warmer parts of the world.

Many millions of years ago, there were many more kinds of reptiles on the earth than there are today. During the period in the earth's history known as the Mesozoic Era, huge reptiles roamed over many continents. Other reptiles conquered the sea and air. About 70 million years ago many reptiles died out, however.

Above: The anaconda is a large snake from South America which kills its prey by constriction or squeezing, before swallowing it whole. The anaconda is also found in rivers.

Left: A cobra rears up in this position before striking at its prey.

Below: Snakes can open their mouths extremely wide. This is how they are able to swallow big prey.

Living Reptiles

The biggest group of living reptiles is the Squamata. These include the snakes and lizards. Snakes are reptiles which have lost the use of their legs over the course of evolution. They move along by means of special movements of their muscular bodies, and they also use their scales to help obtain a grip as they move. A few species swim in the sea.

All snakes are predators, feeding on many different kinds of animal food from eggs to creatures as big as pigs. Some snakes kill their prey before eating it by first squeezing it to death. To do this they quickly surprise their victim and wrap their coils tightly around it. Smaller prey is often swallowed alive. Snakes such as adders, cobras and rattlesnakes first inject their prey with a venom before swallowing it.

Lizards have adapted to many different ways of life. They are also predators but, unlike the snakes, only two species are venomous. The biggest lizard is the Komodo dragon of Borneo. This huge creature measures 3 metres in length. It eats large prey. Most lizards, however, feed on small mammals and birds, as well as on insects and other invertebrates.

The Crocodilia forms the second group of living reptiles. This group includes the crocodiles, caimans, alligators and the gharial. Members of the Crocodilia look very much like their ancestors which existed when reptiles ruled the earth.

Right: The chameleon is a curious lizard which creeps about branches looking for insects to eat. It can swivel both its eyes in different directions. It catches its food on the end of a long, sticky tongue.

Below: The heads of three different crocodilians.

Crocodilians look like huge, armour-plated lizards. They are all adapted to a life spent in water, where they lurk partly submerged beneath the surface waiting for prey. Sometimes they will snatch animals that come to the water's edge to drink. At night they may leave the water to sleep on a sandbank.

The tails of crocodilians are specially flattened for swimming, and the nostrils are placed high on the snout, enabling them to breathe even when lying partly submerged in water.

Crocodilians are found in many parts of the world. They live in the fresh waters of tropical Asia, Africa, Australia and America. One species, the estuarine crocodile, is found in the estuaries of rivers in parts of Asia and Australia. It also swims out to sea.

The most unusual-looking crocodilian is the gharial of India. It has long, thin jaws armed with sharp teeth. Despite its fearsome appearance, however, it catches nothing bigger than fishes.

The Chelonia comprise the tortoises, terrapins and turtles. The chelonians carry on their back a bony shield, and their underbodies are protected by a large, flat, bony plate. When danger threatens these animals can pull their heads and limbs inside their protective armour. Unlike other reptiles, chelonians do not possess teeth, but they have sharp, bony beaks. Also, unlike other reptiles, some chelonians are herbivorous.

Although there are exceptions, most tortoises are land-living creatures, most terrapins live in fresh water, and turtles live in the sea.

The last group of living reptiles is the Rhynchocephalia. Only one living member of this group exists. This animal is called the tuatara. It lives on remote islands near New Zealand, and looks rather like a lizard with spines on its back. It often shares a burrow with a bird, the Manx shearwater.

Below: The giant tortoise of the Galapagos Islands is big enough for a man to ride. A common tortoise is shown by its side.

Birdlife

It would be impossible to mistake a bird for any other animal, for only birds possess feathers. It is feathers which have given birds mastery of the air.

There are nearly 9,000 species of birds throughout the world today, living in every sort of habitat from the seashore to the jungle. The smallest birds are the brilliantly coloured hummingbirds, whose nests are no bigger than a thimble. At the other end of the scale is the ostrich, a flightless bird standing 2.5 metres high.

Birds have adapted to feed on all manner of food. There are some species, the birds of prey, which hunt other animals. Others eat seeds and fruit. A few feed on nothing but insects. Hummingbirds hover over flowers and suck up nectar.

Above: The eagle has a sharp, flesh-tearing beak.

Above: Ducks have wide, flat beaks for sifting mud.

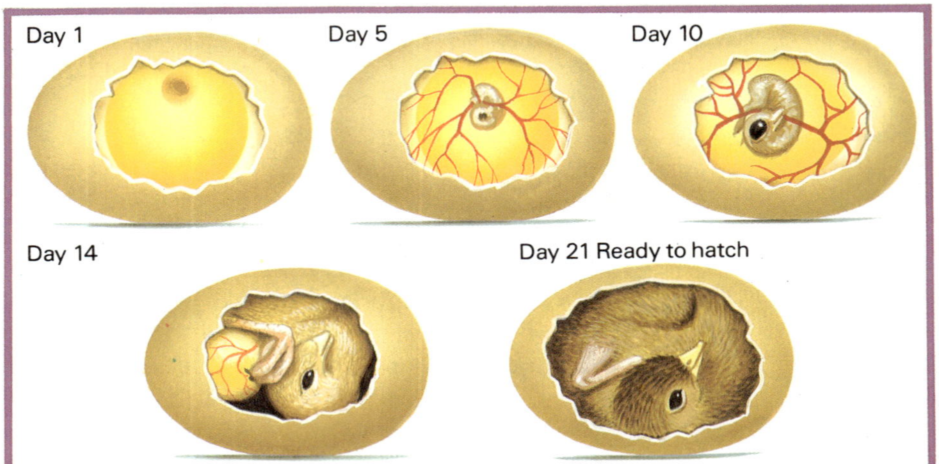

The Development Inside a Bird's Egg

Bird Flight

The ability to fly is the key to the great success of birds. Flight has enabled birds to travel huge distances in search of new territories; to travel from continent to continent during migration; and it has allowed them to escape from their enemies when danger threatens.

For successful flight birds must have lightweight, streamlined bodies. Bird bones are hollow, but specially strengthened, and the feathers help to give them a smooth shape in the air. Lift and motion through the air is provided by the feathers on the wings. The tail is used for steering. Birds which spend hours soaring over oceans have long, narrow wings. Birds which fly fast have sickle-shaped wings. Birds which must fly between the trees have shorter, powerful wings.

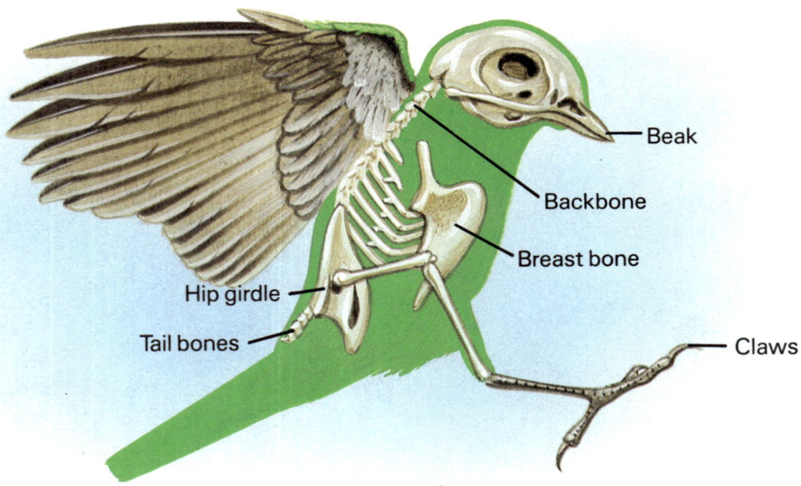

Left: This is how the skeleton is arranged inside a typical bird such as a crow.

Below: Crossbills have short, stout beaks for eating seeds.

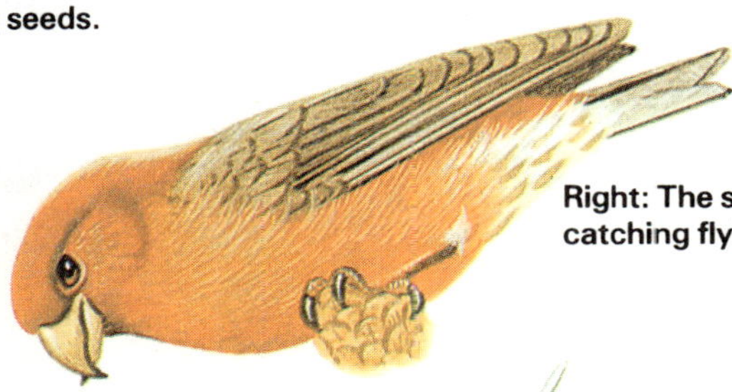

Right: The swift has a very wide beak for catching flying insects.

Above: Skimmers use their beaks to catch fishes near the surface.

Left: The flamingo strains small food items from the water.

Birds and their Young

Many animals build a nest in which to rear their young in safety, but the most familiar of these are birds' nests. Not all birds build nests, however. Some species simply lay their eggs on the ground. The cuckoo is an unusual bird which lays its eggs in the nest of another species.

Before nesting begins, most birds choose a territory and defend it against rivals. The number of eggs laid by the female depends on the species. It may be just one, or as many as 20. Once hatched, the young chicks are fed by their parents until they are big enough to fend for themselves. Most chicks are blind and helpless at birth, but the chicks of waterbirds are born fully feathered and can swim straight away.

Great crested grebes have an elaborate courtship display known as a mating dance.

Right: Many birds, like this whip-poor-will, use their plumage for concealment.

Apes and Monkeys

Apes and monkeys, together with the tree shrews, lemurs, lorises and bush-babies, make up the group of animals known as the primates. In many ways primates are extremely interesting creatures, because man is also a primate. Many monkeys and apes spend their lives in the safety of the treetops. A few, however, have returned to live a life on the ground. Ground-dwelling species include the baboon, the gorilla and, of course, man himself.

Apes and monkeys are intelligent creatures. They have relatively large brains, and forward-facing eyes which help them to judge distances well. Their hands and feet are designed to help them grip branches as they leap from tree to tree. They often live together in well-organized family groups.

These three animals are primitive primates related to the monkeys and apes.

Below: Baboons are large, African, dog-like monkeys which live mainly on the ground. They live in family groups and eat all kinds of food. They defend themselves fiercely if attacked.

Above: Gibbons are apes with very long arms. They swing through the trees with great ease, but can also run along branches. They live in Asian forests and feed mainly on fruit.

Above: The orang-utan is an ape which lives in Borneo and Sumatra.

Above: Chimpanzees are highly intelligent apes which spend part of their lives in the treetops of African forests and part on the ground. They can use their hands in a way very similar to us.

Right: Spider monkeys are extremely agile climbers which can also use their tails to hang on to branches.

Below left: Mandrills are forest-dwelling baboons which live in Africa.

Left: Despite their huge size and fierce appearance, gorillas are shy, plant-eating apes.

Monkeys

Monkeys are divided into two groups: those that live in places like South America, and those that live in Africa, India and Asia. Some monkeys are active during the day, where they search for fruit, leaves, insects or other small animals to eat. Others come out only at night, when their strange calls fill the warm night air.

Apes

There are ten species of apes, all of which live in the tropical forests of Africa and Asia. One group, which includes the gorilla, orang-utan and chimpanzee, is known as the 'great apes'. Apes are the group of primates most closely related to man.

How Animals Communicate

Animals communicate with each other for several reasons. Between members of the same species they may communicate in order to find a mate in the breeding season, or to warn other rivals that they have chosen a particular place as their territory. Watch a bird such as a robin. In the breeding season it will fly from tree to tree, or perhaps perch on a fence, and each time it lands it will sing. In fact, what it is really doing is flying around the boundaries of its territory, telling other robins to keep out.

The fiddler crab communicates by means of 'hand signals'. When the male wishes to attract a female, it sits on the sand and beckons the female with a wave of one of its pincers, which is specially enlarged.

Above: Songbirds, like the American robin shown here, sing to warn other birds that they have chosen a territory, and to attract a mate.

Left: Male moths can pick up the scent given off by females using their feathery antennae.

Below: The male fiddler crab tries to attract females to mate with him by waving one of his pincers, which is specially enlarged.

Whales swimming through the vast oceans of the world communicate by sound. Scientists have often recorded the mournful calls of the humpback whale, which can carry over hundreds of kilometres.

Animals often tell each other about the presence of food, or warn each other of possible danger. Sometimes one bird in a feeding flock will alert the others to a source of food and the rest of the flock will quickly gather to feed. In order to survive, different species of animals have learned to heed each other's warnings. The frantic clap of wings made by a pigeon alarmed in a wood is also a signal to other animals such as squirrels and deer that danger is present. And when lions come to feed at an African waterhole the first grazing animal to spot the danger quickly alerts the others, as zebra, wildebeest, gazelles and even elephants all run to safety.

Many animals are poisonous, and this prevents them being eaten

Right: Timber wolves live in forests and snow-covered wastes. They communicate to other members of the pack by means of special calls. This helps to keep the pack together, even at night.

by predators. Animals which are poisonous, or which are highly venomous, advertise this fact by having brightly coloured bodies. Coral snakes, arrow-poison frogs, ladybirds, kingfishers and wasps are just a few of the many animals which tell other animals that they are poisonous. Sometimes other harmless animals mimic these poisonous species in the hope that they, too, will be left alone by predators.

Right: The skins of arrow-poison frogs contain a very powerful poison, and their brightly coloured bodies warn predators that they are poisonous. The African elephant gives warning to its enemies by drawing its ears forward in a threat display. The caterpillar of the elephant hawkmoth is harmless, but tries to alarm would-be predators by rearing up and showing its eye spots.

THE BEE DANCE

One of the most fascinating examples of communication is to be found among honey bees. Hive members returning from a foray tell other bees about the location of good sources of food, by performing a kind of dance. The speed and direction of the dance indicate the position of the food very accurately. If the food is within 100 metres or so the bee performs a round dance — quick circular motions made first in one direction and then the other. If the food is further away she performs a waggle dance — a figure-of-eight performed while waggling her abdomen. The angle at which she performs the dance tells other bees about the direction of the food.

Right: Honey bees returning to their hive after a food foray inform other hive members about the location of food, by performing a sort of dance.

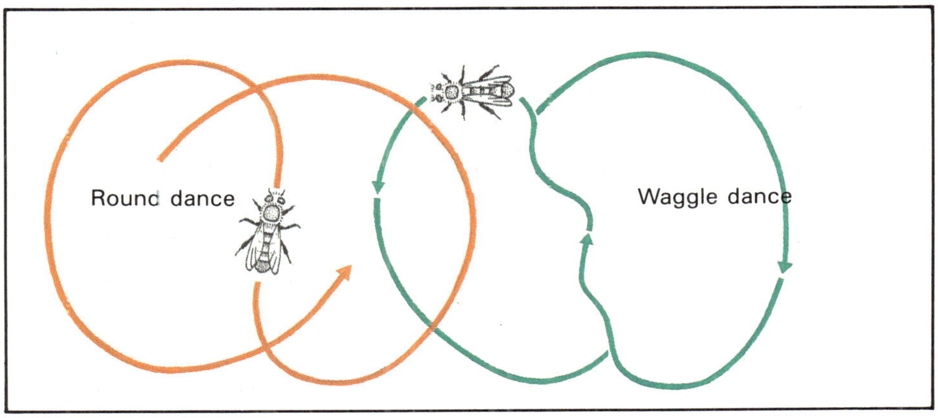

Attack and Defence

For many animals, life in the wild is harsh. Most grazing (plant-eating) animals are preyed upon by meat eaters. Even animals which eat other creatures may themselves become a meal for a bigger predator.

Animals which attack others in order to eat them use many different methods to catch their prey, and an array of weapons with which to overpower them. For example, large predatory mammals such as lions, tigers and cheetahs have powerful limbs, and jaws armed with sharp teeth. Most big cats chase their prey before knocking it to the ground with a blow from their paws. Then they bite the victim in the neck, quickly killing it.

Sometimes animals attack each other for reasons other than to catch food. During the mating season particularly, animals will fight, occasionally to the death, over a mate or a territory.

Above: The trapdoor spider lies cunningly concealed in a trap, waiting for prey. As soon as a likely meal passes, the spider rushes out and overpowers its victim by injecting it with a deadly venom.

Above: The peregrine (left) dives from the air on to its victim. It can fly at such great speed that few birds can escape it. The polar bear (right) catches seals which emerge from ice holes to obtain air.

Left: Dragonfly larvae have special jaws called a mask with which they grab their prey.

Left: Lions hunt their prey together. Some of the lions chase the prey to where other lions are lying in wait for them.

There are many ways in which animals try to avoid being eaten. Some animals are poisonous or distasteful to eat, and warn would-be predators of this fact by wearing bright 'warning colours'. Others are just too big to be eaten; no predator could attack and kill a fully grown rhinoceros or elephant.

Some creatures are quite able to look after themselves. Many types of antelope have sharp horns which can cause severe wounds to unwary predators. Others live in a herd, and are able to run fast. Quite often the predator will single out the weak or old members of the herd and leave the stronger members to escape.

Many creatures, particularly insects, rely on camouflage or a secretive way of life to avoid being spotted by predators.

Mountain hare (summer)

Mountain hare (winter)

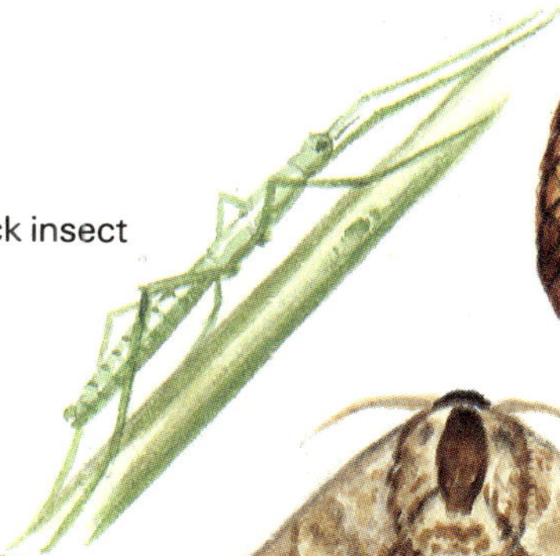

Stick insect

Pangolin

Eland

Porcupine

Hawkmoth

Left and above: Animals like the eland have sharp horns which can inflict a severe wound on predators. The porcupine is armed with a great number of spiny quills. These sharp spines give a painful lesson to any animal attempting to eat the porcupine.

Above: The mountain hare has protective colouration. In winter its coat turns white to match the snow. The stick insect relies on being mistaken for a twig. The pangolin curls into an armour-plated ball, while the hawkmoth uses the 'eyes' on its wings to alarm would-be predators.

Animals and their Young

Above: Many species of snakes coil themselves around their eggs. This helps to protect the eggs from predators, but also keeps the eggs warm during incubation.

Animals must reproduce in order that each species can continue. The simplest animals, like the amoeba, reproduce by simply splitting into two. Most animals, however, reproduce by means of a male and female mating together.

For many animals, the first task in reproduction is to find a safe place to lay their eggs or give birth to their young. In the insect world, many species lay their eggs in holes or crevices, or glued safely to the underside of leaves away from the eyes of predators. Some insects, for example some kinds of wasps, even put in a supply of food ready for the young to eat when they hatch.

Other species of animals may have to fend for themselves as soon as they are born.

Below: Mammals, like the opossum shown here, feed their young with milk, produced in the mammary glands of the female.

Above: Many insects undergo a four-stage life cycle. The adult lays eggs which hatch into larvae. The larvae feed and grow, and turn into pupae. From the pupae emerge new adults.

Right: A reed bunting feeding its chicks at the nest.

Many kinds of birds build nests in which to lay their eggs and rear their young. During spring, both parents will often work ceaselessly hour after hour, building an elaborate nest of twigs, grass, leaves and down so that their chicks will hatch safe from enemies such as snakes or other birds.

Some animals display a remarkable degree of parental care towards their young. We often think of crocodiles as ferocious animals but, as soon as the young hatch from their eggs, the mother crocodile carries her babies gently in her mouth to a safe place.

Once born, the job of finding food begins. Although many creatures must find food for themselves when they are born, most of the more advanced animals, such as birds and mammals, rely on their parents to provide nourishment for them until they have grown big enough to feed themselves.

Above: Scorpions show a remarkable form of parental care. When the young have hatched, they climb on to their parents' back and are carried about, safe from danger.

Below: Many animals, like these brown bear cubs, are taught how to hunt by their parents. Play fighting also helps them to fend for themselves in the wild. The mother watches over the cubs while they play.

Animals on the Move

Each year many animals make long journeys in search of food, shelter from harsh weather or a place to breed. These journeys are called migrations. Among the best-known migrations are the annual journeys from Europe to Africa made by cuckoos, swallows, warblers and many other birds.

Many animals live in parts of the world where the climate changes throughout the year. In the temperate zones these changes are regular and are called seasons, although in the tropics there is little change from one month to the next. As the seasons change the conditions can become less suitable for feeding or breeding; some animals can cope with these changes,perhaps by hibernating, but others overcome the threat of harsh conditions by moving to more favourable areas.

Insect Migration

We normally think of migration as being undertaken only by larger animals, but many insects, especially some butterflies, undergo migrations as lengthy as those carried out by birds and mammals.

The red admiral is a colourful butterfly which is found in north Africa and the Mediterranean. Each spring, however, some of them move northwards into Europe and breed as far north as England and Scandinavia. The following autumn, a few of the new generation fly south to escape the onset of the cold weather. Although many perish on the way, some survive the return journey — an impressive feat for an insect.

Above: The herds of wildebeest on the African plains follow the rains. In this way they can eat the new growth of grass. The animals are constantly on the move, covering hundreds of kilometres a year.

Left: European eels are spawned in the Sargasso Sea. The Gulf Stream carries the young eels to our shores and they move into fresh water. After about ten years they return to the sea to breed.

Above: In some years lemming numbers reach plague proportions. To escape the overcrowding many go on mass migration. At this time predators such as snowy owls and foxes benefit from their abundance.

Below: Bird migrations often involve vast distances and require spectacular navigational skills. Many migrate from northern regions to more temperate areas. Some, like arctic terns, cross to the southern hemisphere for the winter.

Migration of Larger Animals

Both marine mammals as well as land-living species undergo migrations. Seals leave their breeding grounds in spring, and return to warmer seas to spend the winter. When feeding becomes poor many mammals just keep moving until they find better conditions. Herds of animals in Africa follow the rains, grazing the fresh growth of grass that follows. Some reptiles also migrate. Marine turtles haul themselves on to the same beach every year to lay their eggs.

The movements of birds have evolved to become extremely predictable, and they often follow distinct routes over long distances. The arctic tern is famous for its travels from its breeding grounds in the arctic to its wintering area in the antarctic. In its travels it covers over 32,000 kilometres a year, and probably over 160,000 kilometres in its lifetime. As well as travelling further in its life than most other living creatures it also sees more daylight than species which remain in one area.

Nocturnal Life

When darkness falls over the town and countryside, another world comes to life — the world of nocturnal plants and animals. The animals which had been active during the day seek safe places to shelter for the night, and other creatures take their place.

When the sun goes down the temperature drops, and moisture forms on the ground and in the air. These are ideal conditions for the small creatures which thrive in a damp environment. Earthworms, insects, spiders, centipedes and other small invertebrates creep from their hiding places to find food or to mate.

In the darkness other, larger creatures feel safe, too, and leave their burrows to hunt. Mice and voles search for insects, seeds and other food items. They in turn fall prey to the hunters of the night — the predatory animals such as foxes, stoats and owls. Larger creatures such as deer leave the safety of the woodland to graze in the clearings.

Most nocturnal animals are specially adapted for their night-time existence. Badgers and deer have a well-developed sense of smell, for instance. Deer also have acute hearing. Moths can detect the scent given off by females from great distances. Owls swoop down on their prey without warning, for their wings make scarcely a sound as they beat.

Animal Architects

When we visit a cathedral we marvel at the skill of the men who constructed it. But if we consider the building feats achieved by some animals, often working entirely alone, some of these are equally amazing.

Animals build for similar reasons to people; to make a shelter from the elements, protection for themselves or their young, or in order to catch food. Animal shelters and homes range from the little tubes of caddis larvae, to the often complex nests which birds build for their eggs and young.

Some animal constructions are quite small, and are designed to accommodate only their makers. Others, such as termite mounds, are enormous, and provide a home for thousands of individuals. Building material also varies. Some animals use materials they gather from their surroundings, and others produce the building material themselves. Spiders, for instance, make their webs from the silk which they spin inside their own bodies.

Above: The Great Barrier Reef is the only structure built by animals which can be seen from space. It was constructed by tiny marine organisms called coral polyps, like the ones seen here, which encase themselves in a tough chalky shell.

Nests

Birds are among the most familiar of animal architects. At the start of each breeding season, many species of birds build a nest in which to lay their eggs and rear their young. Many nests are quite simple structures consisting of interwoven twigs or grass stems. Sometimes these are neatly arranged, and in other species they are a jumbled mass of material. Often these nests are placed in the fork of a tree or in a crevice, giving the nest support.

Nests are usually built from material which the birds gather close by. This makes the nest quick to build, as well as helping it blend into the surroundings. The long-tailed tit's nest is particularly difficult to spot, since the birds use a mixture of lichens, spider's silk and dry grass.

Below: Many spiders produce sticky silk which they spin into beautiful but deadly webs. These trap flying insects which the spider quickly bites and paralyses. The victim is then wrapped in silk, ready for eating later.

Other Homes

The larvae of the caddis fly are also skilled architects. These soft-bodied freshwater insects protect themselves by building tough tubes in which to live. Each species has its own favourite building material; some use plant leaves, others use sand or snail shells. The tube is open at one end, and the larvae drag themselves around using their front legs.

Termites are tropical insects which live in large colonies. Their mounds, which are usually made from soil, are very strong. They can also become very large, often exceeding 6 metres in height. This feat is all the more remarkable when you consider that the animals which built them were less than 1 centimetre long.

Above: Weavers are birds which build nests together in thorn bushes. The nests are very carefully woven from grass, and often have long entrances designed to prevent predators getting in.

Above: Many wasps are social insects which build papery nests in which to rear their young. They construct layers of hexagonal-shaped chambers in which the eggs are laid and the young wasp larvae grow.

Below: The beaver lodge is a remarkable structure of twigs and logs with its own underwater entrance. Built on a river, the beaver constructs a dam to raise the water level around the lodge.

Animal Curiosities

Throughout the Animal Kingdom there is an incredible array of sizes, shapes, colours and behaviour. At first glance some of these animals may seem particularly strange, but in nature there is always a good reason for any peculiarity. What, to our eyes, may seem strange, is in fact essential for an animal's survival in its chosen environment. The more we study nature the more we realize that there is no 'ordinary' animal. Each species has evolved its own shape, colour and behaviour to ensure its survival.

Nevertheless, there are some animals whose appearance and life styles almost defy the imagination. There are fishes that fly and others that walk on dry land, mammals that can fly in complete darkness, spiders that spin webs under water and many more extraordinary creatures.

Below: Many animals hide from predators, but not so the colourful sea slug which actually advertises its presence. The bright colours warn predators of its unpleasant taste.

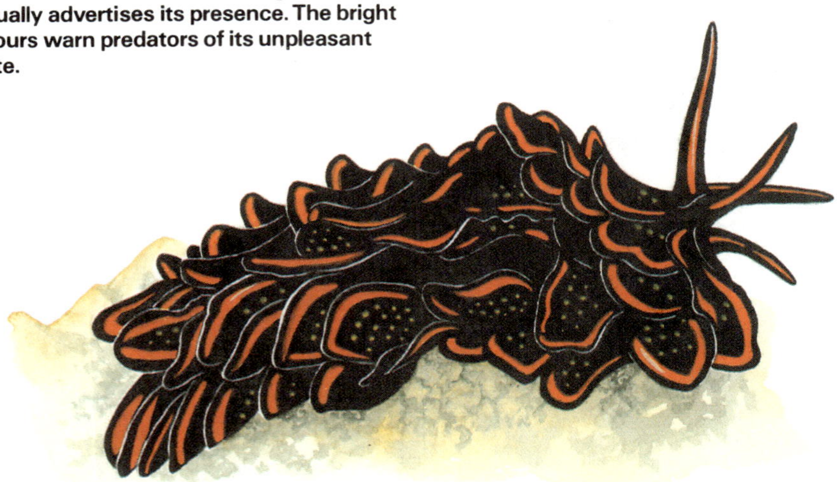

Unusual Spiders

Many spiders spin silk webs to catch their prey. As if this extraordinary feat were not enough, some use their silk in even more unusual ways. For example, the spitting spider does as its name suggests; it spits silk over its prey until it is so entangled that it cannot escape.

The purse web spider does not spin an ordinary web at all. Instead, it lives under ground in a silken tube strengthened with plant fibres. Part of the tube lies on the ground, however, and when a passing insect crawls over its surface, the spider rushes up the tube and grabs the victim through the tube. Needless to say, the tube needs considerable repair after this!

Below left: The water spider spends its life under water, constructing air-bells in which to live and lay its eggs.

Below right: The crab spider pretends to be the inside of a flower. When an insect lands, it is grabbed by the waiting spider.

Odd-shaped Eggs

Bird's eggs are sometimes brightly coloured and sometimes camouflaged to escape the attention of predators, but nearly all eggs are the same shape. The egg of the guillemot is different, however. Its egg is pear-shaped, being blunt at one end and pointed at the other. Guillemots breed on sea cliffs and lay their eggs on steep ledges. The peculiar shape of the egg prevents it rolling off the edge. If it becomes dislodged it just rolls round in a circle.

Above: Flying fish can glide for over 100 metres, using their specially developed fins. This ability helps them escape when being pursued by predators under the water.

Below: Until 1938 the coelacanth was thought to have been extinct for 60 million years. This 'living fossil' is now known to live in deep water in the Indian Ocean.

Coelacanth

Below: The goliath beetle of Africa is the heaviest insect on earth. Weighing over 100 grams it is heavier than many small mammals and birds.

Goliath beetle

Axolotl

Above: The axolotl is a remarkable amphibian related to salamanders. It lives its life as a permanent larva, and uses feathery gills with which to breathe. Even more remarkably, it can even breed while still a larva.

Below: Most species of bat are able to fly in complete darkness, easily avoiding obstacles and catching insects on the wing. They use echolocation to find their way around, although they are not in fact blind.

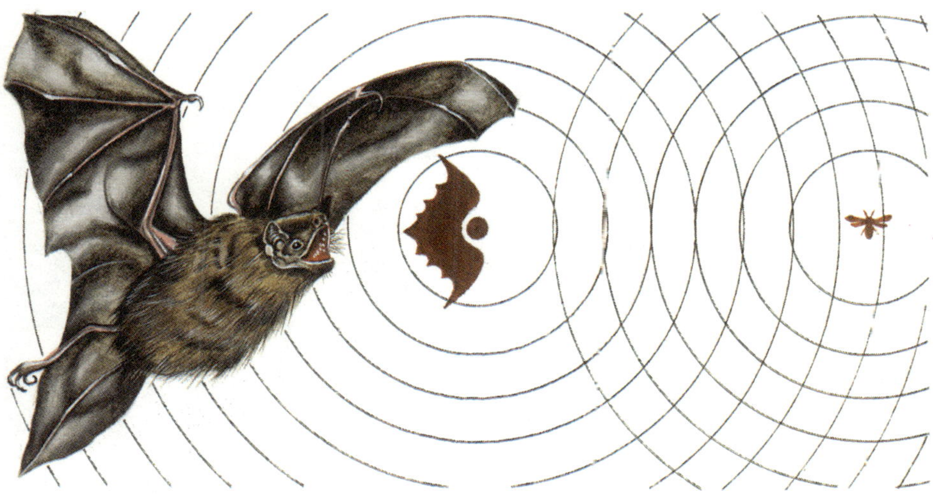

Cactus wren

Above: The cactus wren is a rare example of an animal which uses a tool. By holding a stick in its beak, it prises insects out of crevices in bark.

Living Together

We have already seen how the world of plants and the world of animals are closely interwoven together. Without plants, no animals could survive. Many animals would have no source of food or shelter, and this would mean no food for the other animals which prey upon them. Likewise, many plants rely on animals for their survival. Without insects and other animals, many flowers would not be pollinated nor would their seeds be dispersed. Insectivorous plants such as the sundew and the Venus fly trap must also catch and digest insects and other small creatures in order to obtain the nitrogen which is essential for their healthy growth.

Many animals also need the help of other animals to help them avoid predators or to help them find food. For this reason some species join together in great herds. Sometimes, however, animals which are quite unrelated join together to improve their chances of survival.

Below: Grazing animals, like these herds of buffalo on the American plains, join together in great herds for protection. The herd guards the youngest members which might fall victim to predators, and each animal is always on the lookout for any signs of danger.

PLANT AND ANIMAL PARTNERSHIPS

Although most of the partnerships in nature are between different species of animals, or between different species of plants, there are some partnerships in which a plant and an animal live together. Many aquatic animals, such as corals or the freshwater creatures known as Hydra, contain green algae within their bodies. The algae have a safe place in which to live, and in return they provide oxygen and absorb the various waste materials produced by the animals. Within the bodies of many animals live bacteria. These help to break down the cellulose found in plants and so enable the animals to digest grass.

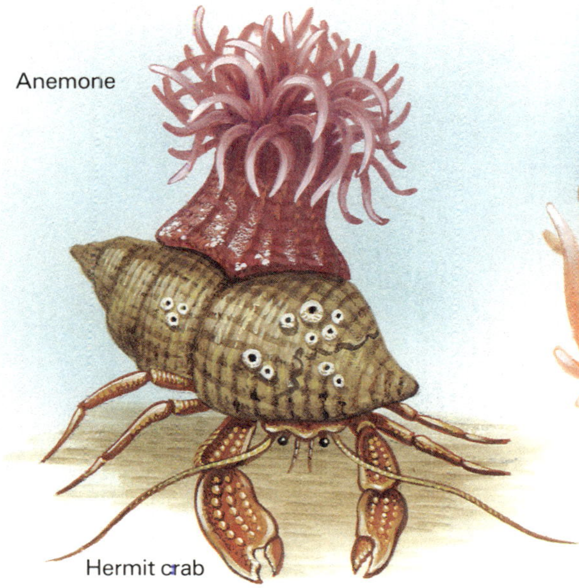

Above: The hermit crab often carries an anemone around on its shell. The anemone protects the crab, and in return shares some of the crab's food.

Above: Clown fishes are brightly coloured inhabitants of coral reefs. They feel quite safe swimming among the deadly stinging tentacles of anemones which also inhabit the reef. The anemones let the clown fishes swim among their tentacles to escape predators, in return for ridding them of parasites.

Animal Partnerships

In the Animal Kingdom there are many examples of animals living together for the benefit of one, or both, partners. The simplest form of this behaviour is when one animal spends its life living close to another animal for its own benefit. Birds such as cattle egrets ride on the backs of grazing animals as they walk slowly through the long grass. As they walk, they disturb insects and other creatures which the egrets then swoop down to feed on. Although the grass-eating animals do not themselves benefit from the association, they do not suffer either.

Sharks are often attended by fishes known as remoras. The remoras attach themselves to the sharks by means of suckers on their heads. They eat the scraps left over by the shark when it feeds, which in return uses the remoras as a 'vacuum cleaner' service, for they remove parasites from the shark's skin.

Sometimes two different species of animals rely so much on each other for food or protection that they are unable to live so successfully on their own. This condition is know as symbiosis. There are many examples of symbiosis in the Animal Kingdom. The partnerships shown on this page between the hermit crab and the anemone, and between the clown fishes and the anemone are two.

Top left: Oxpeckers are African birds which are allowed to feed on the skin parasites of rhinoceroses. In return, the oxpeckers alert the rhinoceros of danger.

Left: Spur-wing plovers and dikkops help keep crocodiles free of parasites.

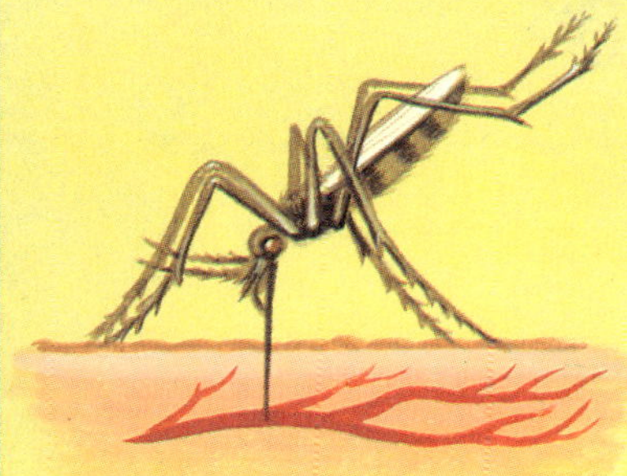

Female mosquitoes transmit the disease called malaria. The mosquitoes feed on the blood of man, which they obtain by inserting their mouthparts into blood vessels near the skin. As they do so, they inject into the bloodstream tiny, single-celled parasites called trypanosomes. Trypanosomes enter the red blood cells of humans and multiply. After a time, they burst from the cells and into the bloodstream, producing the familiar malarial fever. Some of the trypanosomes pass to another mosquito when it bites a victim, ready to be passed on to another human.

Index

Illustrators
Mike Atkinson, Jim Dugdale, Ron Jobson, Linden Artists Ltd., John Marshall, Bernard Robinson, Frederick St. Ward, Mike Saunders and David Wright.

Cover illustrations by
Graham Austin/Garden Studio

 Published in Great Britain by Cliveden Press, an Egmont Company, Egmont House, PO Box 111, Great Ducie Street, Manchester M60 3BL.

Printed in Singapore.

ISBN 0 7498 0397 5

Reprinted 1992

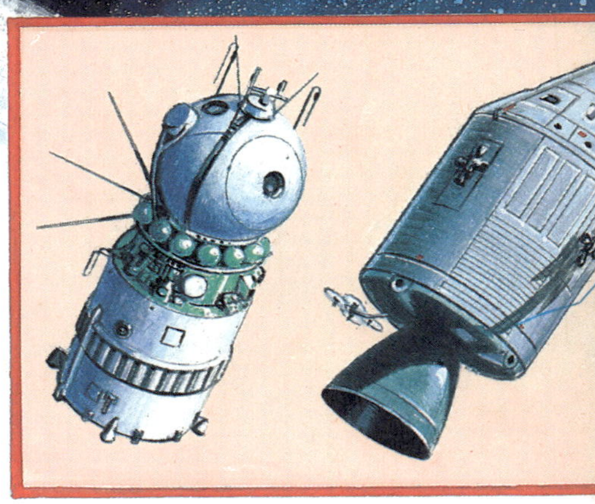

THE WORLD OF
Science

CLIVEDEN PRESS

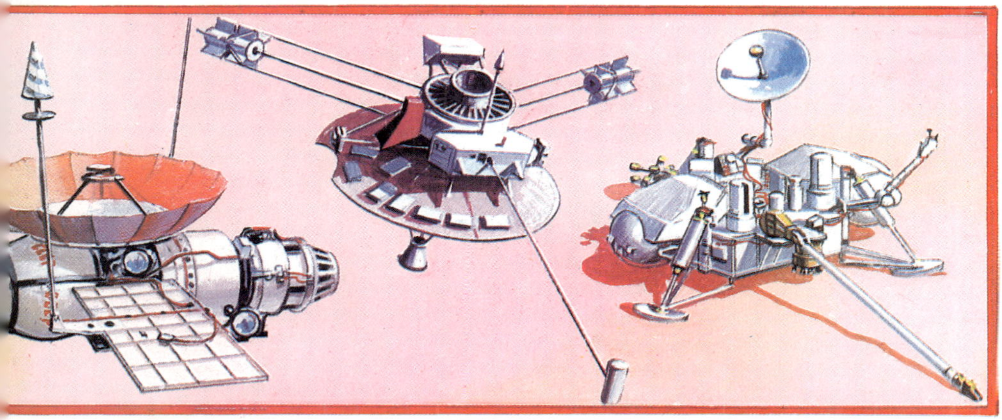

Contents

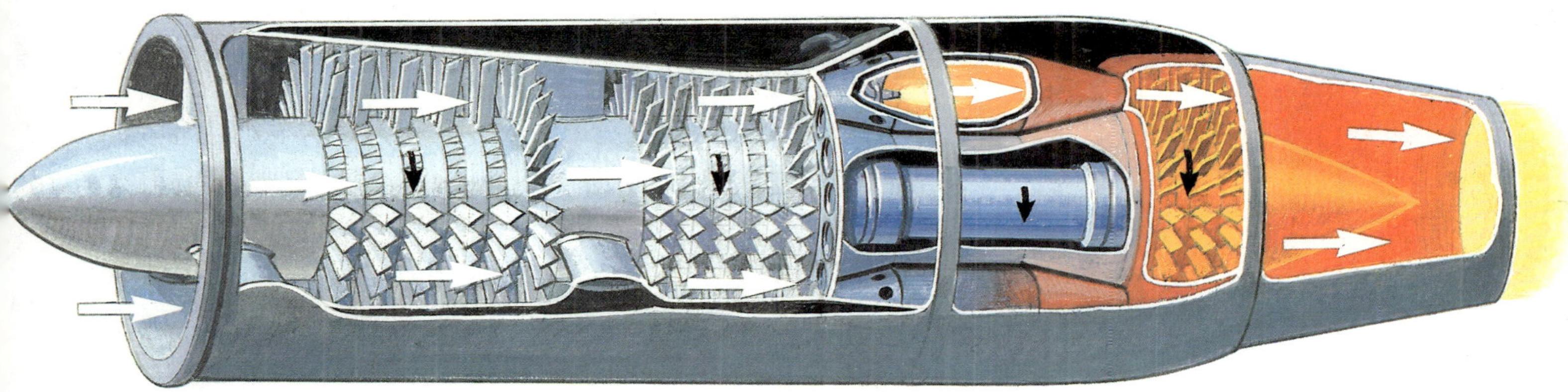

Solids, Liquids and Gases

When scientists talk about matter, they mean everything in the world. And all matter can be divided into three groups: solids such as iron or wood, liquids such as water and oil, and gases such as air or steam. Ice is solid water. When ice is heated it melts to become liquid water. When the liquid is heated to 100°C it boils and becomes a gas – steam.

Solids tend to resist being pulled or pushed out of shape; they usually keep the same size and shape, no matter where they are. Liquids have no shape of their own. They take the shape of any container they are poured into. Gases do not keep either their shape or their size. They expand to completely fill anything they are in.

The reason why different materials behave in different ways is because of the tiny atoms that make them up. Iron is different from gold because it is made up of a different kind of atom. The way in which the atoms are packed together decides whether a substance is a solid, a liquid or a gas.

Water is a strange liquid. It is one of the very few things that grows bigger (expands) when it freezes. That is why huge icebergs float, even though most of the bulk is under the surface.

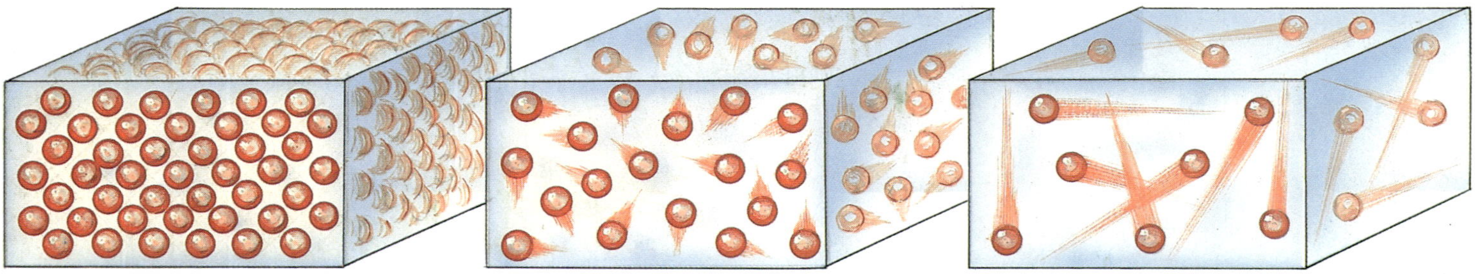

Solid

A solid keeps its shape

Liquid

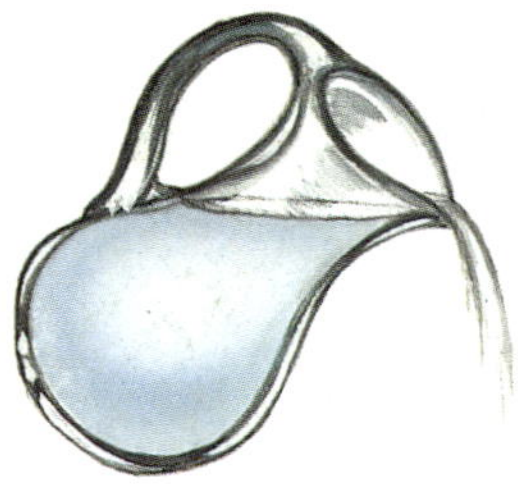

Liquids hold together but take the shape of a container

Gas

When gases are released, they expand for ever

How solid something is depends on how closely packed the atoms in it are. In a solid, the atoms are close together and fixed in position. This is why it is difficult for a solid to change its shape or its size. In a liquid, the atoms are less tightly packed and can move about a bit. When a solid is heated, the atoms in it move more and more until they form a liquid. They move apart but do not escape from each other completely. If we go on heating a liquid, the particles in it move faster and faster. After a while they move so quickly that they escape from the surface of the liquid and become a gas. This is called *evaporation*. When the liquid gets hotter still, the particles escape so quickly that the liquid bubbles. This is called *boiling*. When water boils it turns into the invisible gas, steam.

Solids

Solids are solid because of the way their atoms and molecules are arranged. Ice, water and steam are all the same from a chemical point of view – they all contain the same kind of atoms and molecules. The difference lies in the movement of the molecules. In ice, the molecules are held tightly in a definite pattern – what is called a *crystal lattice* – by strong forces between the neighbouring molecules. Snow is a mass of beautiful ice crystals, each six-sided and no two of them are alike (see above). Although molecules in ice do not move about, they still vibrate a little.

Liquids

Some substances such as water, oil and the metal mercury are liquid at ordinary room temperature. A liquid is similar to a gas because its atoms and molecules are not fixed together in any particular way. But it is also similar to a solid because it has a definite volume.

The molecules of a liquid are often attracted to the molecules of other substances. And this attraction is greater than the attraction between neighbouring molecules of the liquid. This is why liquids will rise up a narrow tube. It is called *capillary action.* Water also has a 'skin' called *surface tension.* This is why the pond-skater (above) can walk on the surface.

Gases

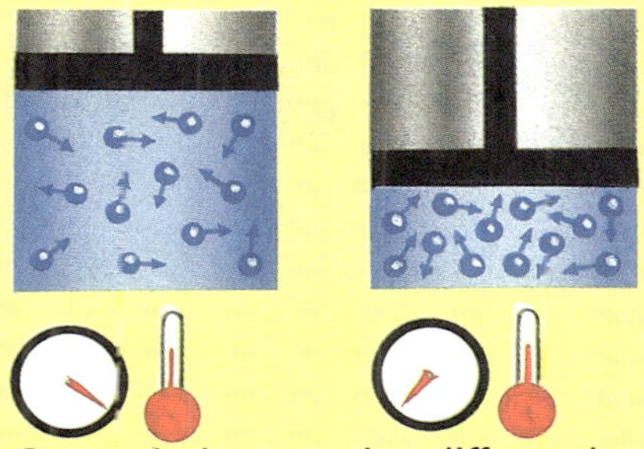

Gases behave quite differently from solids and liquids. They are the lightest and most movable form of matter. Any substance on Earth can be turned into a gas if it is heated above its boiling point. Iron becomes a gas if it is heated to about 2900°C. The temperature of the Sun is so high that all the matter in it is in the form of a gas.

Every gas consists of molecules flying about and colliding with each other. The pressure of a mass doubles if its volume is halved (above). But the temperature must remain constant.

The first man to study light and tell people how it worked was Isaac Newton. In 1665, the great scientist shone a beam of light through a glass *prism,* shaped like the one on the left. He found that the light that came out of the prism had been broken up into all the colours of the rainbow. Newton had discovered that ordinary white light is made up of all the rainbow colours added together. We see a band of colours because our eyes see different wavelengths of light as different colours. Each colour has its own wavelength.

Light and Colour

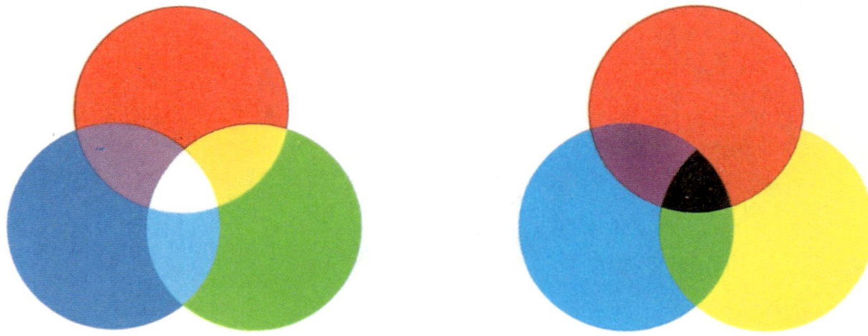

MIXING LIGHT
The three primary colours of light are red, green and blue. Any other colour can be made by mixing these colours. When red, green and blue lights are mixed, the result is white light.

MIXING PAINTS
When paints, inks or dyes are mixed, the basic colours are cyan blue, magenta red and yellow. Cyan and yellow give green. If the three basic colours are mixed, the result is black.

Without light, all life on Earth would come to an end because all the plants and trees would die. People have always realized how important light is, so they tried to find out what it was. Some thought it was made up of tiny particles, others thought it was a series of waves. Today, scientists think that light is neither completely a wave nor completely a stream of particles. It is a cross between the two. But they are still not quite sure what light really is. They do know that light waves are *electromagnetic,* just like radio waves and X-rays.

Radio waves can be kilometres long. Light waves are very short – about five-hundred-thousandths of a centimetre long. This wavelength is important because it limits the size of things we can see through a microscope. If we look at anything about the size of the wavelength of light through a powerful microscope, it is fuzzy.

Invisible Light

Different kinds of light can be seen by different animals. Most humans see all the colours from red through orange, yellow, green, blue to violet.

More than a hundred years ago, scientists tried to find out about the spectrum colours by putting a thermometer in each colour coming from a prism. It was found that as the thermometer was moved from violet to the red end, the temperature increased slightly. But, even more surprising, when the thermometer was placed beyond the red, where there was no visible light, the temperature was even hotter. There is a hot, invisible radiation just below the red. This radiation is called *infrared* radiation (*infra* means below). Some animals such as the pit viper can actually 'see' these infrared rays, which are really heat rays.

At the other end of the colour spectrum are other beams of 'light' that we cannot see. They are just above the violet, so they are called 'ultraviolet'. Bees can see ultraviolet light although humans cannot.

Light travels in a straight line at a speed of about 300,000 km per second. But there are ways of making light change direction. One way is to bounce it off the surface of something. This is called *reflection*. We can see the Moon and the other planets because they reflect the Sun's light. They have no light of their own.

Seems Straight

Place a coin in a cup and move your head back until the coin is just no longer visible. Now, keeping your head steady, pour some water into the cup. Hey presto! The coin appears. This magic is caused by *refraction*. Refraction causes a light beam to bend as it passes from one substance to another. When the light beam from the coin leaves the water and enters the air, it bends so that you can see the coin. The coin looks as though it is in the position at the end of the dotted line in the diagram below. The amount by which light is refracted depends on two things: the angle at which the light beam strikes the second material, and the speed at which the light is travelling. If the light beam goes straight from one substance to another at right angles there is no refraction. If you put the coin in the cup and look straight down on it as you pour in the water, the coin doesn't appear to move. Light travels at its fastest in a vacuum (empty space). In air it travels almost as fast. But in water and glass, light slows down. In fact, in going through some kinds of glass, light travels at only about half its speed in a vacuum – 300,000 km per second.

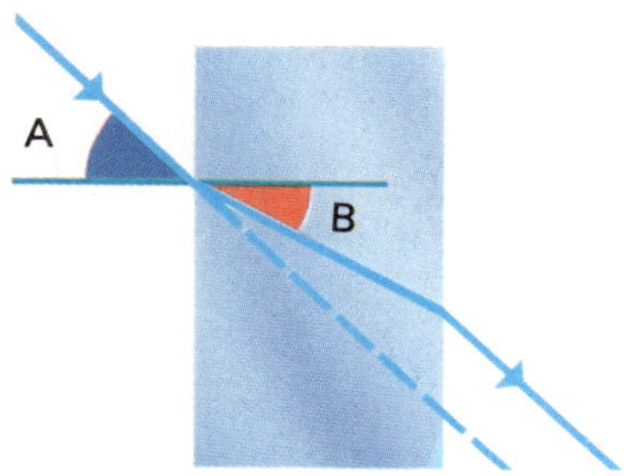

When light passes through a piece of glass it is *refracted.* Angle A is called the *angle of incidence.* Angle B is the *angle of refraction* (the angle by which the beam bends).

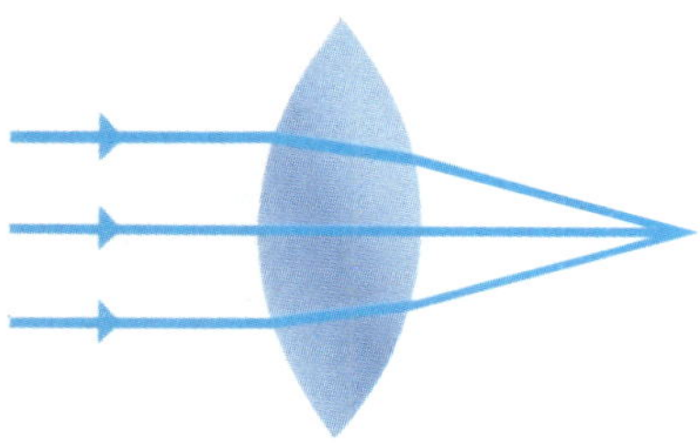

Light is bent in *lenses.* A lens shaped like the one above (convex) brings light rays together at a point called the *focal point.* A magnifying glass is a *convex lens*.

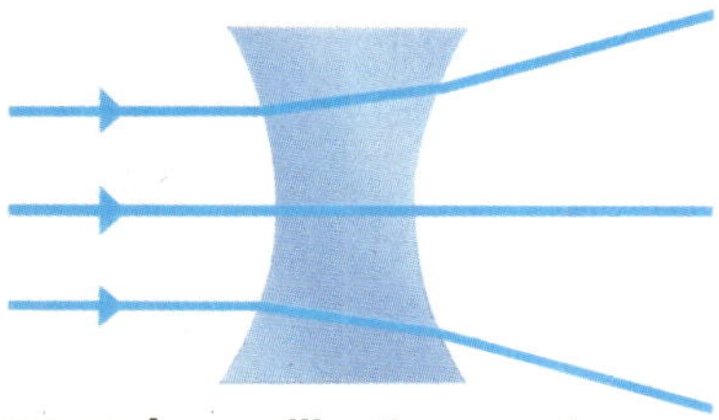

***Concave lenses* like the one above make light rays spread out. If you look through one, things look smaller. Lenses of this kind are nearly always used with other lenses.**

Very Special Light

The laser is one of the most important inventions of the 20th century. A laser beam is a beam of very pure light. We have seen that ordinary light is made up of all the colours of the rainbow. Each colour has a different wavelength. A laser beam has waves that are all the same. The waves rise and fall in step. This makes the laser's narrow beam very powerful. Because of the laser's power and accuracy, it is being used for more and more tasks. It can drill a tiny hole in a diamond, slice through steel plates, help in delicate surgical operations and carry thousands of telephone messages through fine fibres of glass.

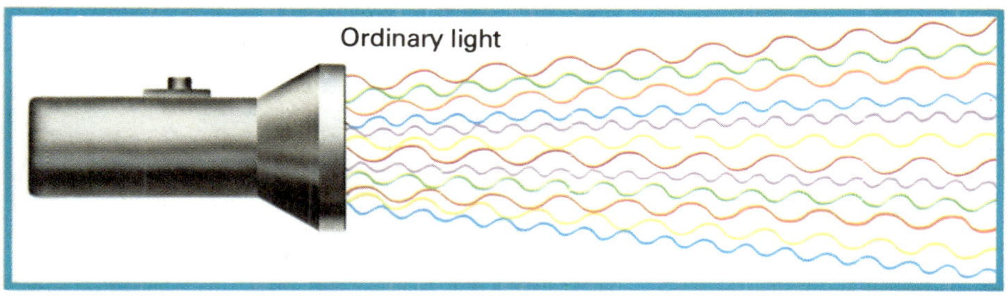

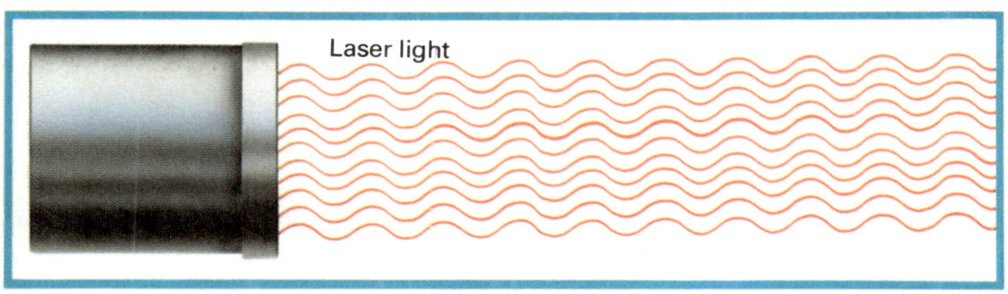

The Force of Gravity

Everything in Earth is pulled downwards by a strange force called gravity. The pull of gravity is always towards the centre of the Earth. A stone dropped from someone's hand in England falls to the ground in the same way it would fall in New Zealand on the opposite side of the world. Both stones fall towards the centre of the Earth. And gravity isn't a force that happens only on Earth. Everything in the universe is attracted towards everything else. It is only because the Earth is so big and so close to us that we notice gravity here. The more massive a body, the more material in it, the greater its gravitational pull on other bodies.

The Sun is much more massive than the Earth and all the other planets put together. So the Sun's enormous gravitational pull holds all the planets in place as they circle their big parent body. It is incredible to think that our mighty Earth, speeding along at 30 km per second, is held in its orbit by this invisible bond. In exactly the same way, Earth's gravity holds the Moon in place in its monthly journey around us.

An astronaut, hundreds of miles above the Earth, is weightless because he is so far from the Earth's gravitational centre. He feels he is floating and not moving, but both he and his spaceship are travelling at about 30,000 km per hour. The pull of gravity holds him in orbit around the Earth.

Gravity decreases with distance from the Earth and the same object weighs less and less.

The Tides

Although the Moon's gravity is much less than the Earth's, it still affects us. Tides are caused mainly by the gravitational pull of the Moon, and, to a lesser extent, by the pull of the Sun. When the Moon is overhead, the oceans' waters are drawn towards it, causing a bulge, which is balanced by another bulge on the opposite side of the Earth. High tides are called *spring* tides. They happen when the Earth, Moon and Sun are in a straight line (see diagram). The combined gravitational pull of the Moon and the Sun makes high tides even higher and low tides even lower. The smallest tides – called *neap* tides – happen when the pull of the Moon is at right angles to that of the Sun. Spring tides happen about twice a month, about the time of the full moon and the new moon. Neap tides happen around the first and last quarters of the moon.

Tides occur twice every 24 hours 50 minutes, the time taken for one complete orbit of the Moon around the Earth.

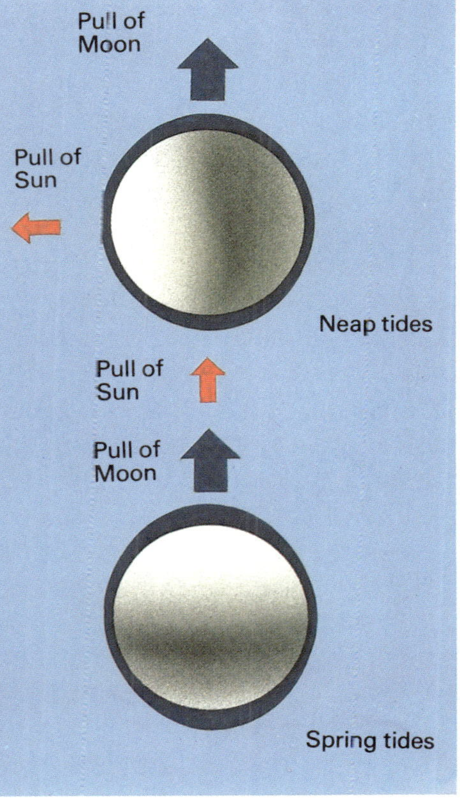

The great Italian 16th century scientist Galileo was the first to prove that all objects fall to the ground at the same speed. People knew that a cannon ball falls faster than a feather. But Galileo proved that this was because the feather was slowed down by air resistance. On the Moon, where there is no air, the cannon ball and the feather fall at exactly the same rate.

Losing Gravity

The force of gravity grows less and less the further apart bodies are. When people go up in a spaceship the pull of Earth gravity gets less the higher they go. After a while, the Earth's pull is so small the astronauts do not notice it. They are weightless and live in a strange floating state where there is no 'up' or 'down'.

But what happens if the spaceship goes further and gets close to the Moon? Then the astronauts and their ship begin to come into the pull of the Moon's gravity. With no rockets firing, the spaceship will be pulled faster and faster towards the Moon. If the astronauts land on the Moon they find they can do things they cannot do on Earth. They can lift rocks six times as heavy. Even in their bulky spacesuits they can jump much higher. This is because the gravity of the Moon is only a sixth of Earth gravity. The Moon has only a sixth of the mass of our Earth. If an astronaut who weighed 65 kg on Earth weighed himself on the Moon, the scales would show a weight of only 11 kg. On the other hand, if people ever reach the giant planet Jupiter they will find things much more difficult. If you can jump a height of one metre on Earth, you could only jump 28 cm on Jupiter. And if it were possible to stand on the surface of the Sun, you could not even jump to the height of 3 cm!

A World of Atoms

All substances that exist – human beings, animals, plants, wood, rocks, air, metals, water – are made up of matter. Wood is solid matter; water is liquid matter; and air is gaseous matter.

The smallest piece of a substance that is still recognizable as that substance is called a molecule. The molecule in turn is made up of a number of atoms. Different substances are made up of different kinds of atoms.

The simplest substances are those whose molecules are made up of just one kind of atom. They are called the chemical elements and can be regarded as the building blocks of matter. The metals iron, copper and gold are elements. So are carbon and oxygen.

Other substances have molecules made up of combinations of different atoms. They are called compounds. Atoms of iron, for example, combine with atoms of oxygen to form the compound iron oxide, or rust.

It was once thought that atoms were the smallest particles of matter that could exist – 100 million atoms, side by side, measure only 1 centimetre! But we now know that atoms are made up of even smallest particles and we can even split them.

1

2

3

Above: In a solid (1) the molecules are close together and attract one another strongly. They remain firmly in place. In a liquid (2) the molecules are farther apart. They still attract one another, but not strongly, and they are free to move around. So a liquid can flow. In a gas (3) the molecules are far apart and exert little attraction on one another. They travel very fast.

Animal

Vegetable

Mineral

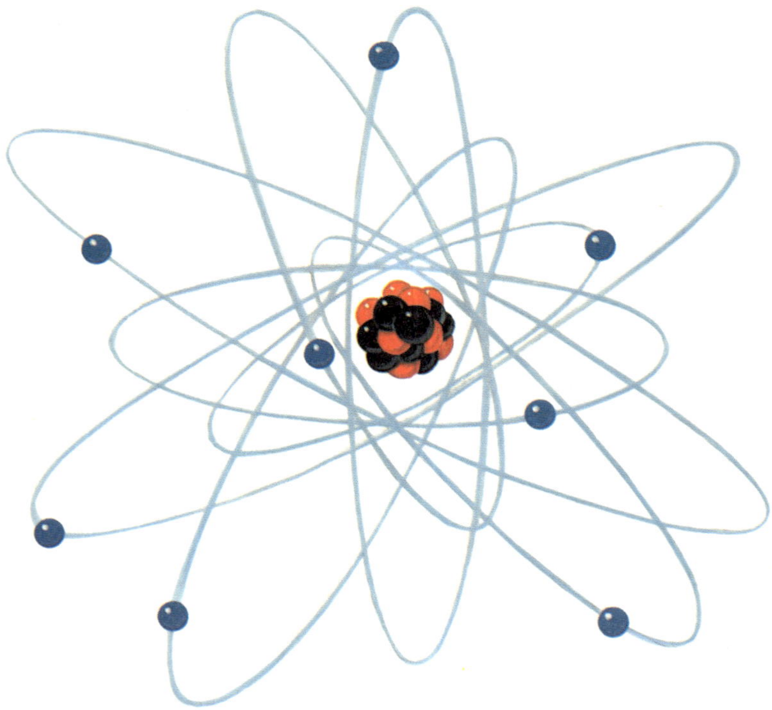

Left: All things on Earth, be they animal, vegetable or mineral, are made up of millions upon millions of atoms. Every atom is constructed in a similar way. The main part is the nucleus. This is made up of tiny particles called protons and neutrons. Around the nucleus circle a number of even tinier particles called electrons. There are as many electrons as there are protons. The protons have a positive electric charge and the electrons have a negative charge. So the atom as a whole is electrically neutral.

Below: The menacing cloud from an atomic-bomb explosion. An atomic explosion has many thousand times the destructive force of an ordinary explosion. It also produces deadly radiation and fallout. Fallout is dangerous radioactive dust carried by winds and falls far away from the site of the explosion.

Below: Energy is released when atoms split, or undergo fission. A uranium atom may undergo fission when it is bombarded by a neutron. It splits into two, releasing energy as light, heat and radiation. Two or more neutrons are also produced in the process. These neutrons may in turn go on to cause fission in other atoms, causing what is called a chain reaction. The energy released when a chain reaction occurs is enormous.

Bottom: The chain reaction is a useful source of power when it can be controlled. This is done in a nuclear reactor. In a reactor, the core contains the uranium 'fuel'. The chain reaction is controlled by means of control rods. A liquid or gas coolant circulates through the core and extracts heat. It gives up this heat to water in a heat exchanger. The steam produced then goes to turbine generating machinery.

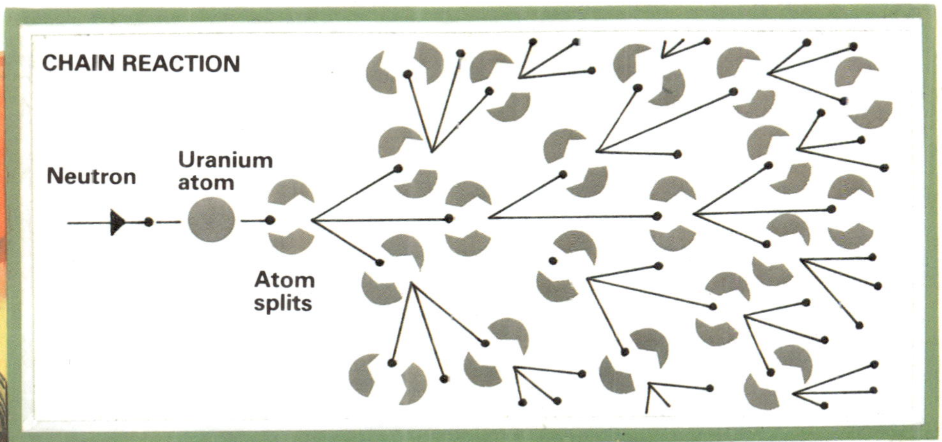

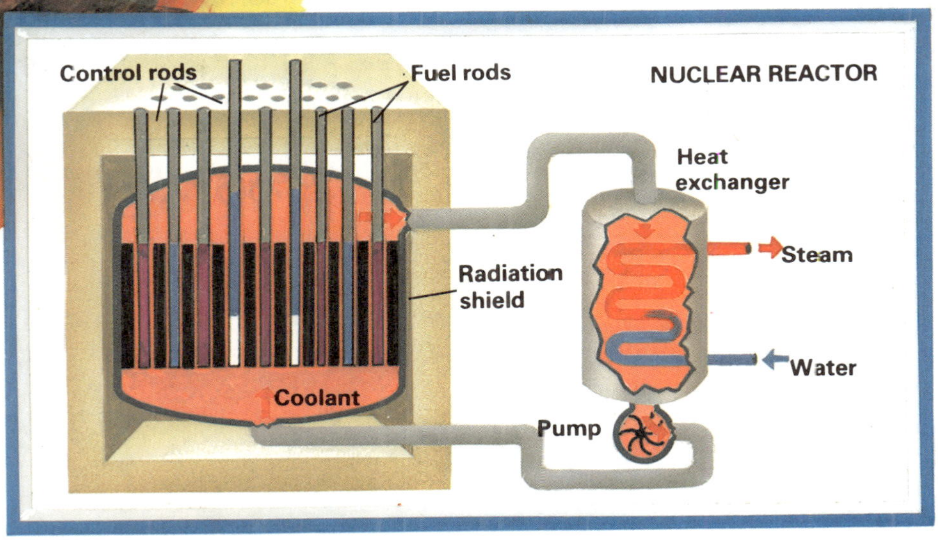

NUCLEAR FUSION

Fission is a nuclear process that occurs when very heavy atoms, such as uranium, split. The opposite kind of process can also occur. Very light atoms can combine to form heavier ones. This process is called fusion. Fusion also releases enormous amounts of energy.

It is in fact fusion that provides the energy to make the Sun and the stars shine. Inside the Sun, at temperatures of millions of degrees, atoms of hydrogen combine, or fuse together, to form atoms of helium.

Scientists on Earth have imitated this process and produced the hydrogen bomb, the most terrible weapon of all. They are now trying to find ways of controlling fusion to produce useful power. They are trying to do this in two ways – with powerful magnetic machines called tokamaks, and with lasers.

Energy and Power

Warm swamps covered many regions of the Earth some 300 million years ago (main picture). In them grew huge ferns and horsetails. When these plants died, they fell into the swamp and began to decay. Over the years the remains dried and hardened into coal, now found sandwiched between the rock layers (inset above). The organisms that lived in ancient seas also died and decayed, and we find their remains today as oil and natural gas, trapped in the rock layers (inset below).

We could not live the way we do today without a plentiful supply of energy. Most of the energy we use comes from oil, coal and natural gas. These are known as fossil fuels because they are the remains of organisms – plants and animals – that once lived. And they are burned to release their energy.

Most oil, or petroleum, is made into fuels that are burned in engines, to power cars, trucks, locomotives and aeroplanes. These fuels include petrol, kerosene and diesel oil. Most coal is burned in power stations to produce electricity. The heat from the burning coal heats water in a boiler into steam. The steam then spins a turbine, which in turn spins a generator to make electricity. Electricity is a very convenient way of 'carrying' energy from place to place.

Some power stations use another kind of 'fuel' to produce heat for the boilers. This is nuclear fuel, such as uranium. Under certain conditions uranium atoms can be made to

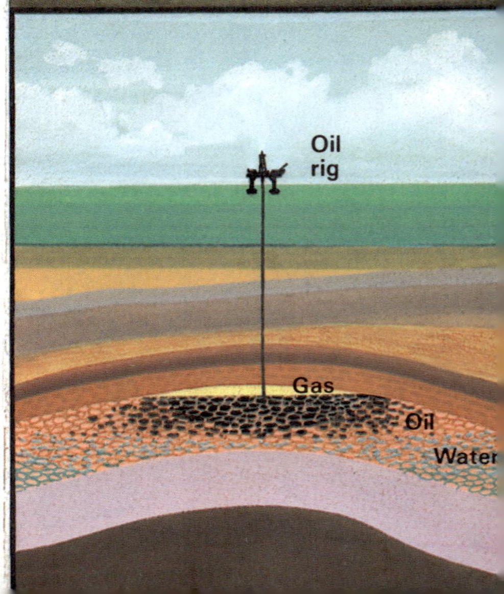

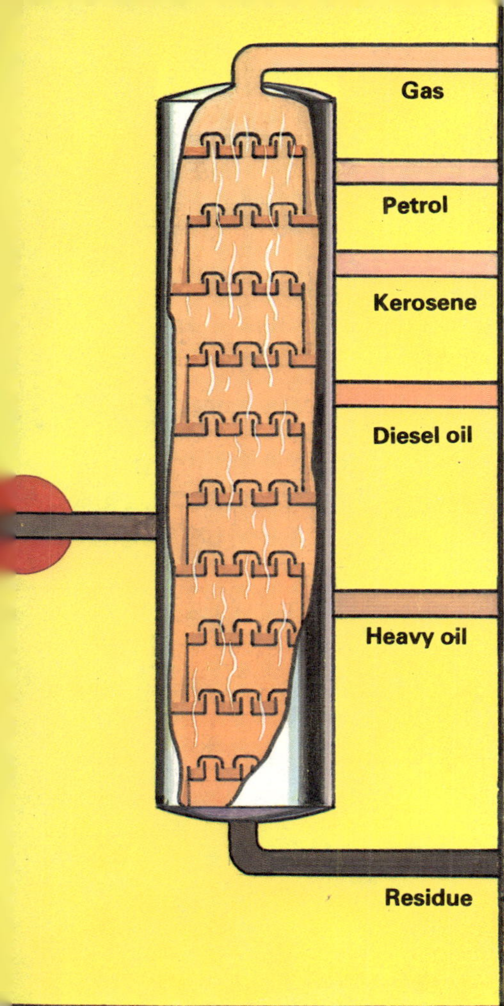

split, and this releases large amount of heat. Nuclear power is an important energy source.

Alternative Energy Sources

Supplies of fossil fuels and uranium are obtained from the ground. Eventually these supplies will run out. Then we must find alternative sources of energy. We are already using one – flowing water. We harness this power in hydro-electric ('water-electric') schemes. The water spins water turbines, which drive the electricity generators.

Schemes to harness other natural energy sources are also well under way. Engineers are building huge wind turbines, wave-power devices and solar 'power towers'.

Left: Before it can be used, crude oil must be refined, or processed, in an oil refinery. The first stage is distillation, which takes place in this kind of tower. Oil vapour passes through the tower, and the various substances it contains separate out into various parts, or fractions.

Below: Some regions of the world are blessed with plenty of sunshine, a 'free' source of energy waiting to be tapped. This can be done with a solar power tower. Large numbers of mirrors reflect sunshine onto a boiler at the top of a tower. This heats water in the boiler into steam.

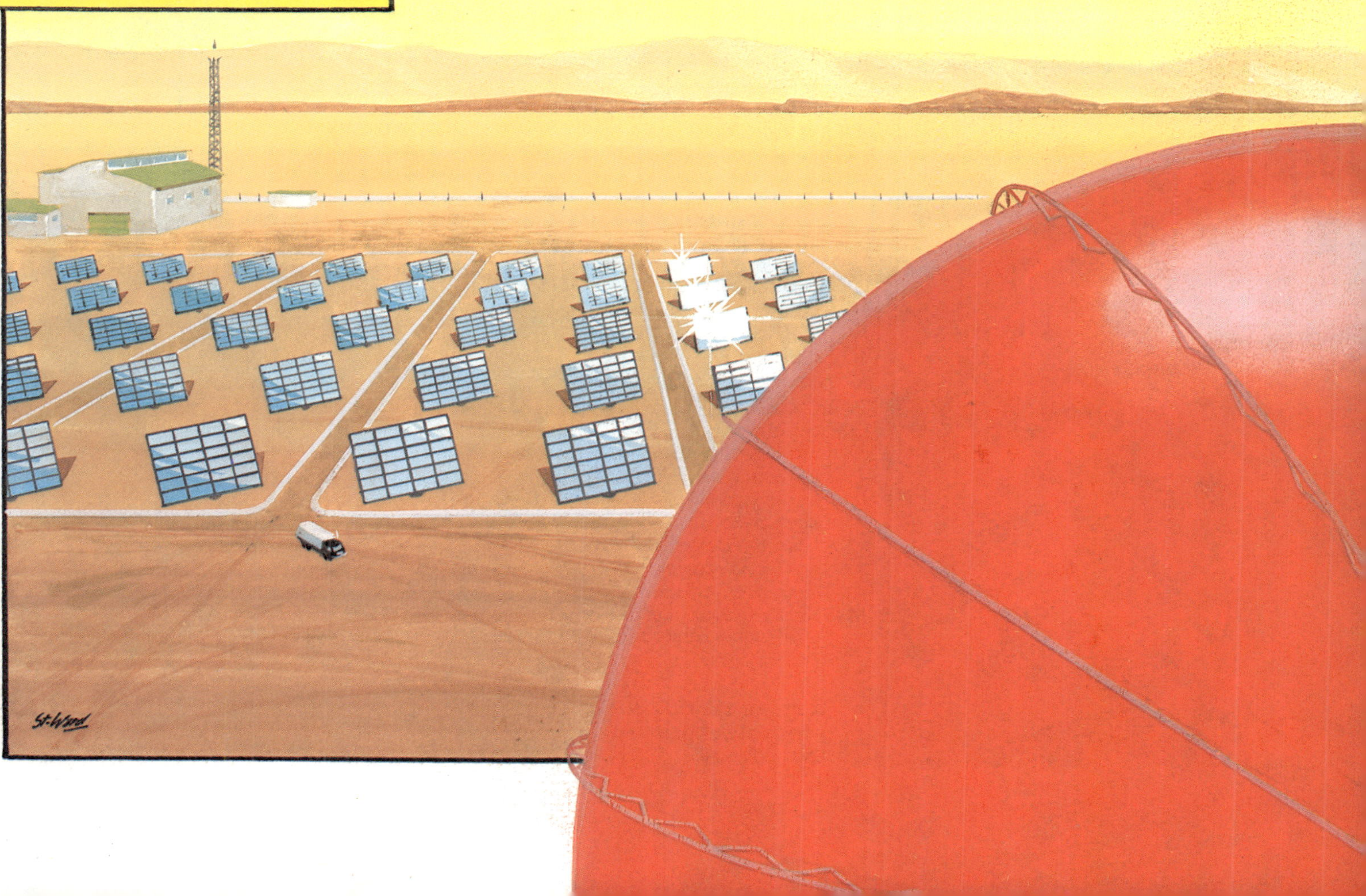

Heat – Molecules in Motion

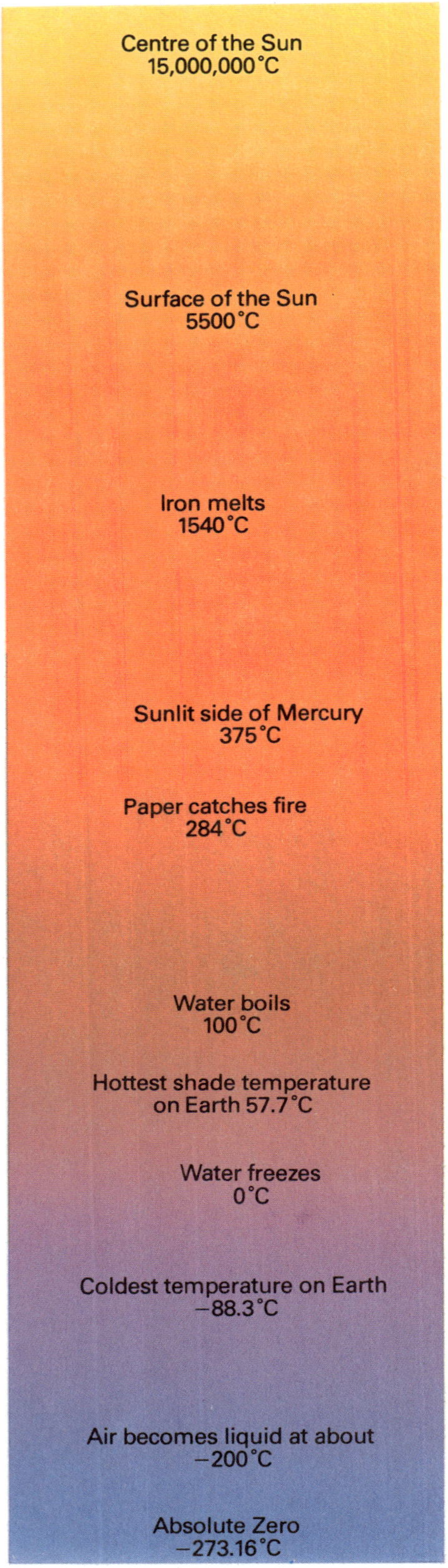

What is heat? Scientists say it is a form of energy – the energy of moving atoms and molecules, that everything is made up of. Atoms and molecules are always on the move, and the heat of anything is simply a measure of how fast they are moving. The faster they move, the hotter a body is.

We measure heat with *thermometers*. Water boils when the thermometer shows 100 on the Centigrade scale (100°C); it freezes at 0°C. Our bodies use the food we eat as fuel to keep our temperature at about 37°C. But temperature and heat are not quite the same thing. If we put two pots on the stove, one full of water, the other with very little water, it will take much longer for the full pot to boil. This means that much more *heat* has to be put into the full pot to get both pots to 100°C.

Heat passes from one place to another in three different ways. They are called *convection, radiation* and *conduction.*

Convection carries heat by circulating it in *convection currents.* A room heater, for example, warms the air around it. This heated air expands and rises and is replaced by cooler air. Then the new cooler air is heated and rises. This means that a constant current of air carries heat all over the room. Convection currents also occur in liquids (right).

With radiation, heat travels through empty space. When something gets hot, its moving atoms and molecules make invisible waves of radiant energy. These waves are also called *infra-red rays.* The heat that reaches us from the Sun has travelled by radiation rays at the speed of light. Heat waves and light waves are exactly the same except for their different wavelengths.

Conduction is the movement of heat through a material or from one body to another if the bodies are touching. If we place one end of a metal spoon in boiling water, the handle of the spoon soon becomes too hot to hold. The heat from the water has travelled up the spoon by conduction. Some materials such as metals are good conductors – they conduct heat easily; other substances such as wood are bad conductors.

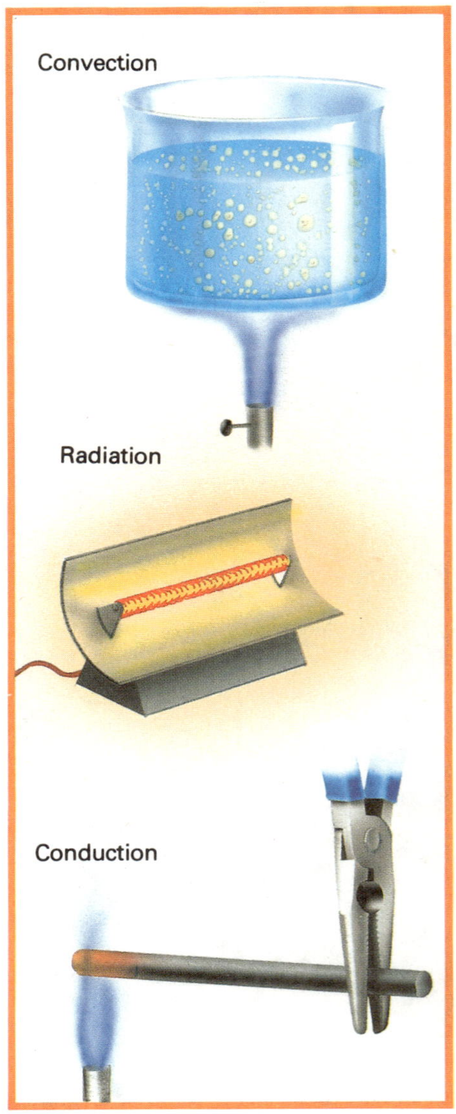

Left: An example of the tremendous range of temperatures experienced in the universe.

Hot and Cold

Steel begins to melt at a temperature of about 1500°C, but this is very chilly compared to the heat of the Sun. Inside the Sun the temperature is about 15 million degrees. Other stars are much hotter still. There appears to be no limit to how hot it can get.

Cold is different. The coldest place on Earth is a chilly −88°C (88 degrees below zero). But the thermometer would have to drop to −183°C before the air started to freeze. At −273°C, *absolute zero* is reached. At this temperature everything would be frozen solid. Nothing would move. Even the atoms would stop moving. But it is not possible to reach this temperature.

Nearly everything grows bigger when it is heated. If you place a thermometer in hot water, the atoms in the mercury move faster and faster and take up more space. The mercury expands and moves up the thermometer's stem.

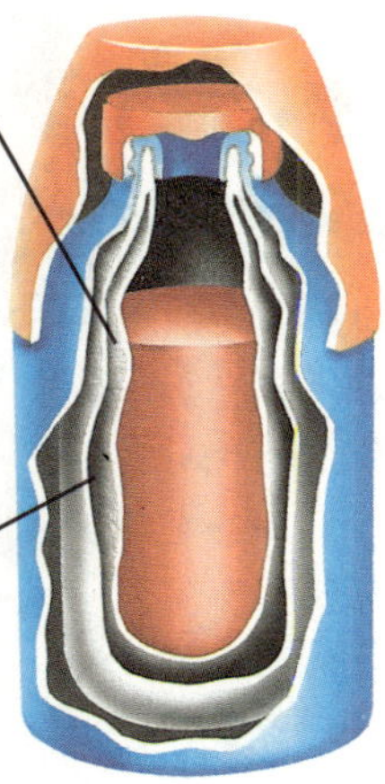

Vacuum flasks keep things hot or cold for a long time. There is a vacuum between the double walls of the flask to stop heat loss by conduction. The container is also silvered to help stop loss of heat by radiation.

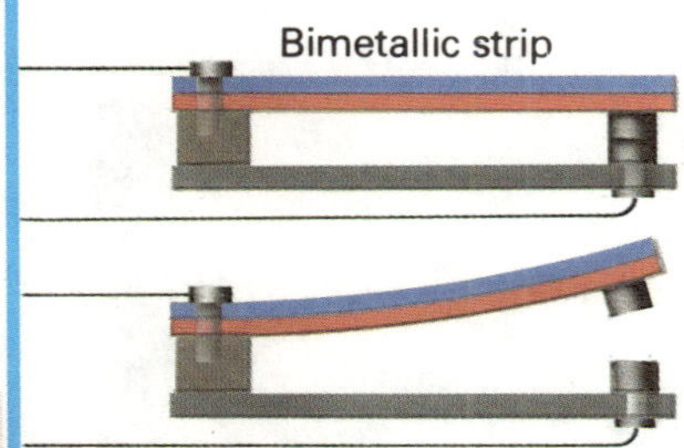

Thermostats make use of the fact that some substances expand and contract more than others when they are heated. They are used in heating systems, cookers and irons to switch the heat on when the temperature falls too low, and to switch it off again when the required temperature is reached. They are also used in refrigerators.

Many thermostats have a *bimetallic strip* made of two different metals such as brass and iron fastened together. As the temperature rises, the brass expands more than the iron. This makes the strip bend upwards. The electrical contact is broken and the heating current stops flowing. As the bimetallic strip cools down again the brass contracts until the two metals are the same size once more. The contact is made and the heating current flows once more.

A fire-fighter wears a special suit so that he can walk through flames and remain unharmed. The suit is made of asbestos, a substance that is a very poor conductor of heat. The silvery surface of the suit reflects heat away.

Chemical Reactions

Chemistry is the study of substances. It looks at what they are made of and how they split up or join together with other substances. Everything around us is made of chemicals. The water we drink, the salt and sugar we eat are chemicals. So are the proteins that make up most of all plants and animals.

There are just over a hundred basic chemicals called *elements*. Everything is made up of these. Iron, oxygen, carbon, gold and silver are all elements. And elements are made up of tiny atoms. Each element has its own kind of atom that is different from the atoms of all the other elements. When the atoms of two or more different elements join together, they form a chemical *compound*. Water is a compound of the elements of hydrogen and oxygen. Two atoms of hydrogen join with one atom of oxygen to make a *molecule* of water.

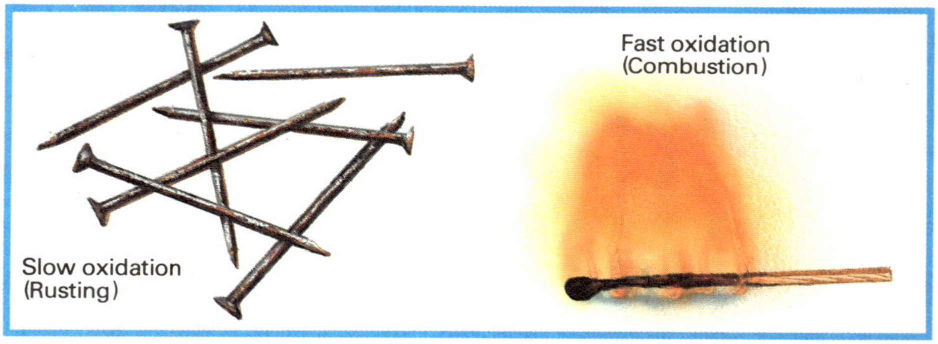

Some compounds are very complicated. Each molecule of sugar, for example, contains 22 hydrogen atoms, 11 oxygen atoms and 12 carbon atoms. Sugar, starch and alcohol all have molecules that contain hydrogen, oxygen and carbon, but in different proportions. It is the different proportions that make the three substances different.

Chemists use symbols to name substances. Chemical formulas show the elements that make up the substances. The symbol for the element hydrogen is H; for oxygen it is O. The formula for water is H_2O.

Vast quantities of chemicals are used in the modern world. Soaps and detergents, dyes and acids, polishes, artificial fibres and explosives – all these things and thousands more are products of the vast chemical industry.

When something burns very quickly indeed, we say it 'explodes'. The exploding force in fireworks (above) comes from the rapid burning of gunpowder. Gunpowder is a mixture of sulphur, saltpetre and charcoal. When an explosion happens, a quite small quantity of explosive such as gunpowder burns in a flash and turns into a large amount of hot gas. It is this expanding gas that sends rockets into the air. The brilliant colours of fireworks comes from metallic salts that are added. Calcium salts give a red colour; sodium, yellow; barium, green; and copper, blue and green.

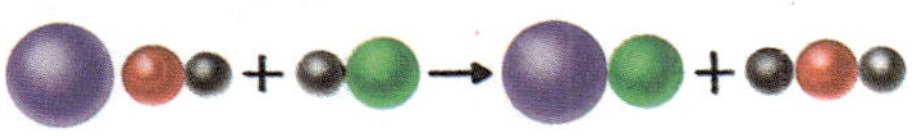

Acids turn litmus paper red. *Bases* turn litmus paper blue. Acids and bases neutralize each other – they cancel each other out. Bases that dissolve in water are called *alkalis.* When a base neutralizes an acid it makes salt and water only. If we take a solution of sodium hydroxide (a base) and add it to hydrochloric acid in the right quantities, the result is neutral. We are left with sodium chloride (table salt) and water (see above).

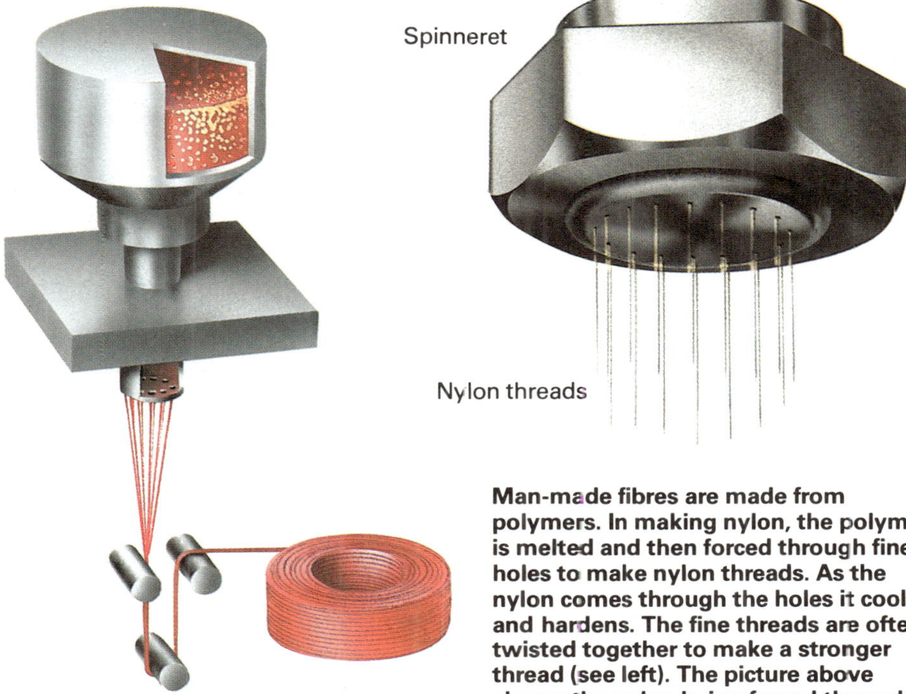

Man-made fibres are made from polymers. In making nylon, the polymer is melted and then forced through fine holes to make nylon threads. As the nylon comes through the holes it cools and hardens. The fine threads are often twisted together to make a stronger thread (see left). The picture above shows the nylon being forced through the holes in a *spinneret*.

Substances that are made up of long chains of carbon atoms are often called *polymers.* Cotton is a natural polymer because the fibres of cotton are made up of a polymer called *cellulose.* Cellulose is a compound with long chains of carbon atoms. Nowadays, chemists make artificial polymers. For example, molecules of the gas ethylene join together in a long chain to make polyethylene – the plastic we call Polythene (see above). There are many different plastics that rely on the joining together of carbon atoms. Plastics have countless uses.

Slow and Fast Burning

Oxygen is the most plentiful of all the elements in nature. Although it is a gas we cannot see, it accounts for about half the weight of most rocks and minerals. A fifth of the air we breathe is oxygen, and nearly all living things need it.

Oxygen is a very active chemical. It combines with many other chemical elements to make a very large number of compounds. These compounds are called *oxides*. The process in which they are made is called *oxidation*. Slow oxidation happens when iron is in damp air. This produces *iron oxide*, which we call rust. When oxygen and another element are combined rapidly, light and heat are given off. We call fast oxidation *combustion*, or burning.

Magnets

A magnet is any piece of metal that will attract or pull towards itself iron, steel or a few other metals. Magnets can be of different sizes and shapes, and they can be strong or weak. The ends of magnets are called their *poles*. One end is called the *north-seeking pole* (N); the other is the *south-seeking pole* (S).

Magnets are very important. They are used every day in telephones and in the loudspeakers of television sets and radios. And they are a vital part of the big generators that make our electricity.

The magnet on the right is called a *horseshoe magnet*. If we hang chains of pins from it, each pin becomes a small magnet; each with its own north and south poles.

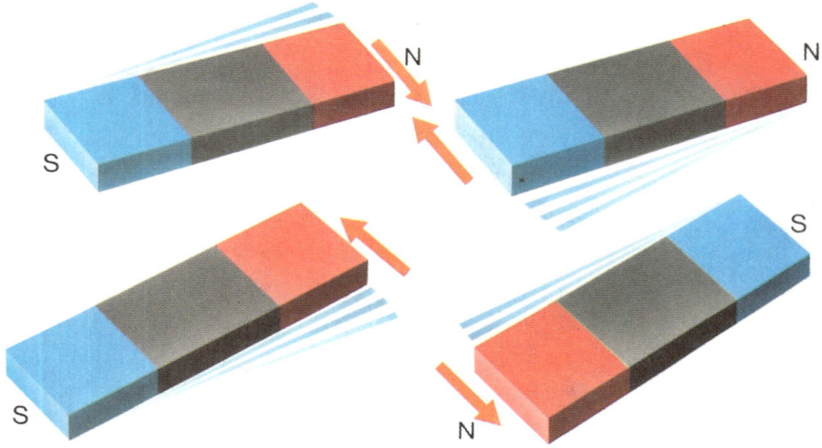

The magnets on the left are called bar magnets. If we place the south pole of one magnet near the north pole of another, the magnets will be attracted to each other. If we place the north pole of one near the north pole of another, they will push each other apart. We say that unlike poles attract and like poles repel. All magnets have more magnetic pull at their ends than at their middle.

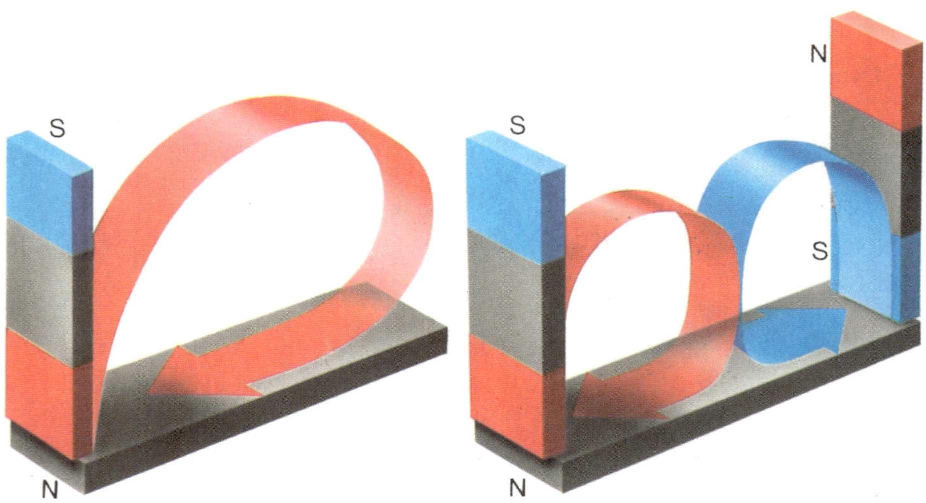

There are several ways of making magnets. One way is to stroke a permanent magnet across the metal to be magnetized, usually a piece of iron. (Soft iron is easier to magnetize than hard steel.) The iron must be stroked in one direction only, as shown in the pictures on the left.

A weak magnet can also be made by placing the iron in line with the Earth's magnetic field and hammering it. An electric current flowing in a coil around the metal will also magnetize it.

Magnets can be made to lose their magnetism by hammering them or by heating them in a flame.

Magnetic Fields

Every magnet has an invisible *magnetic field* going through it and around it. The field around a bar magnet can be seen if we lay a sheet of paper over the magnet and sprinkle iron filings on the paper. When the paper is tapped, the iron filings will move into lines, called *lines of force,* around the magnet. Most of the lines cluster round the ends of the magnet where the magnetism is strongest.

The magnet on the right is called a *horseshoe magnet*. If we move a small compass around in the horseshoe magnet's field and note the way the compass needle points, we can draw a pattern of lines as in the picture.

The Earth has a weak magnetic field, rather like that of an enormous bar magnet. Compass needles all over the world point north and south because of the Earth's magnetism.

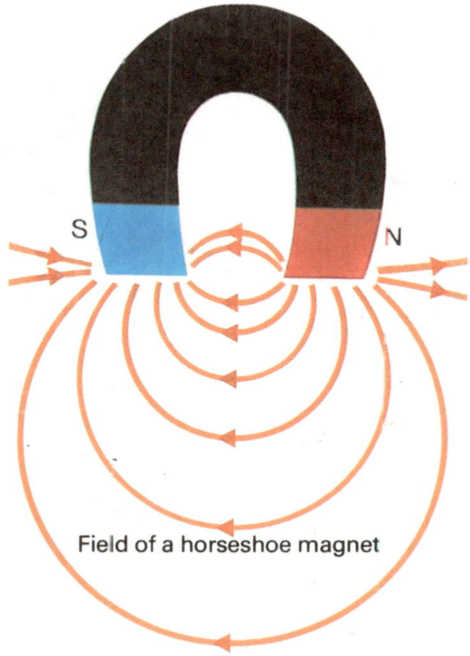

Field of a horseshoe magnet

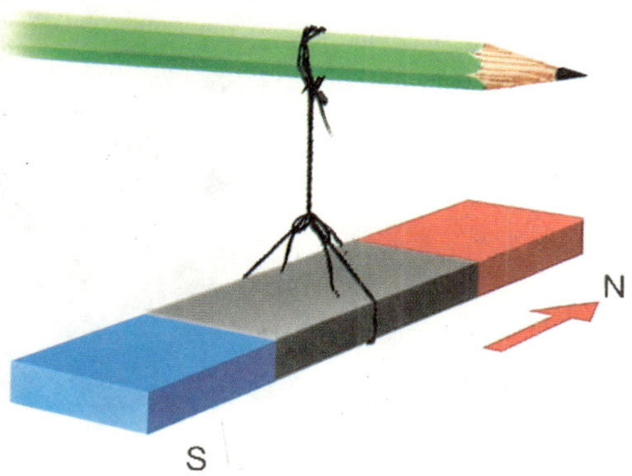

If a bar magnet is suspended as shown above, it will always come to rest pointing in a North–South direction. And always the same end of the magnet points North. A compass (below) is really a small, lightweight magnet. It is pivoted so that it can move freely. The Earth's North pole always attracts the magnet's South pole.

The end of the magnet that points North is called the magnet's *North-seeking pole*.

Compass

The Earth's magnetic field

Making Electricity

When ancient people saw lightning flashes in the sky, they thought the gods were angry. They did not know about electricity, but they noticed that some things seemed at times to attract other things. The ancient Greeks knew that if they rubbed a piece of amber with a woollen cloth, straw and dry leaves were attracted to it.

Today, we know that both the lightning and the amber's attraction are forms of electricity. Lightning happens when clouds store up too much electricity. Electric sparks which we call lightning shoot from the clouds to other clouds or to the ground.

An electric current is a movement, or flow, of tiny particles called *electrons*. Electrons are particles of negative electricity that circle around the centre of every atom. In some materials, a few of the electrons are only loosely held to their atoms. They are free to jump from atom to atom. When they do this, an electric current flows. An electric current is started by a battery or electric generator. If the

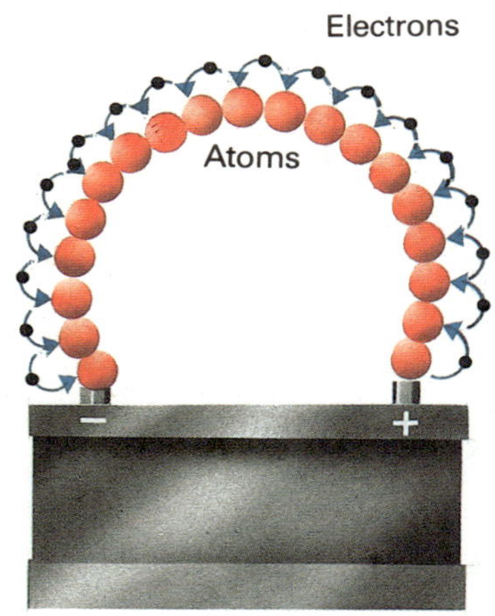

When the terminals of a battery are connected by a wire, an electric current flows from one terminal to the other. Most metals are good conductors of electricity – especially copper and silver. Wires are usually made of copper. The copper atoms have *free* electrons that can be pushed on to the next atom in the line. Another free electron is pushed from that atom, and so on to the other battery terminal. This is an electric current.

Electricity can be produced by separating two different metals with a solution that conducts electricity. A 'dry' cell is not really dry. It is filled with a damp chemical paste. The positive terminal is a carbon rod. The zinc container is the negative electrode.

An accumulator or battery contains cells made of lead plates in dilute sulphuric acid. Car batteries usually have six 2-volt cells. They are connected in series to give 12 volts.

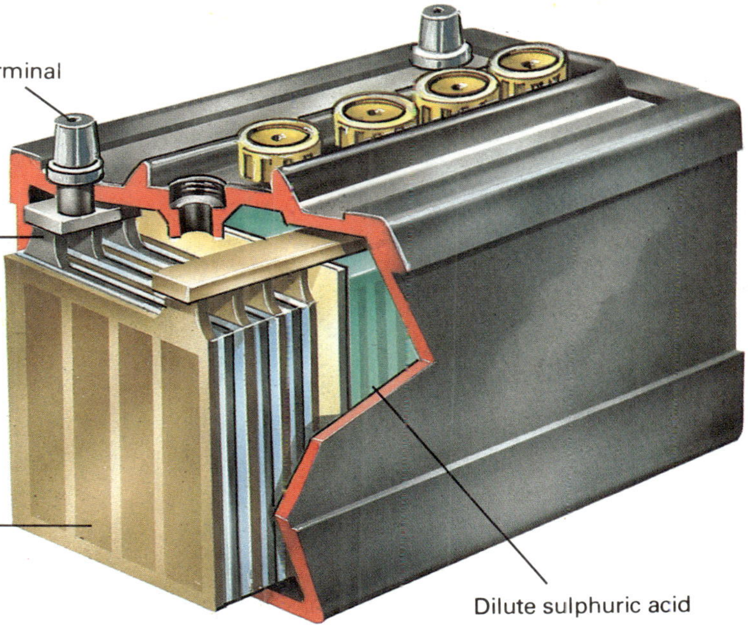

terminals of a battery are connected to each end of a piece of wire, electrons are pushed from the first atom in the line to the next, and so on along the wire – all in a flash of time. Wires which carry electric current are often made of copper. Copper, like most metals, is a good *conductor* of electricity. It has lots of free electrons.

Batteries and Generators

Batteries make electricity by chemical action. The most common kind of battery – the flashlight battery – is really a *dry cell*. When the chemicals in the cell are used up, the cell is dead and is thrown away. A battery is two or more cells working together.

A car battery is different. It is filled with dilute sulphuric acid in which are lead plates. When this kind of battery runs down it can be recharged by connecting it to an electric current. This makes the chemical action go backwards. The electrons are put back where they were and the battery can produce current again.

An electric generator is a machine that turns mechanical energy into electrical energy. The simplest generator is a loop of wire that is turned between the poles of a magnet. When the wire cuts the lines of force between the magnet's poles, an electric current is produced in the wire. This is the principle of the electric generator.

The diagram below shows a very simple electric generator. A loop of wire is turned between the poles of a permanent magnet. As the wire cuts the lines of magnetic force between the magnet's poles, an electric current is produced in the wire. The current is taken from the wire loop through carbon brushes that rub against metal rings. Large generators have thousands of loops of wire and produce a very large, steady current.

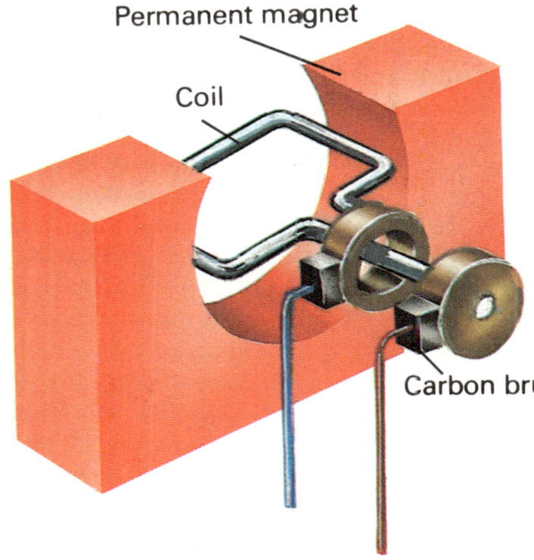

Putting Electricity to Work

When an electric current goes through the fine coiled wire *filament* inside a light bulb, the filament gets hot and glows with light. The filament is made of tungsten, a metal that does not melt easily when it is hot. The bulb has no air in it and has other gases to help stop the filament burning out.

Electricity is the most useful form of energy. It can be taken easily by cables to our homes, factories and offices and there used to produce light and heat or run machines.

The electricity we use is produced at power stations by large generators. These are machines that are turned by power from coal or oil to make electricity. Electricity flows along wires as a current. A current of electricity must have a completely unbroken path. If we could follow a current from the generator, it would travel across country through heavy overhead copper wires and along underground cables to our house. There it would go through a meter that would show how much current went through it; through fuses, to an electric light bulb. After the current has passed through the bulb and produced light, it goes all the way back through a separate wire to the generator in the power station. All this happens in a flash.

Most electricity is used to make things move. What do vacuum cleaners, food mixers and tape recorders have in common? They all have *electric motors* inside them to make things go round (see opposite page).

Some of the most powerful electric motors are used to drive electric trains. The electricity can be carried to the train's motors in different ways. Some railways have overhead wires above the track. A metal bar reaches up from the train and slides along the wire to collect the electric current. This is called a *pantograph.* Other trains get their power from a third rail placed beside the track.

HOW AN ELECTRIC MOTOR WORKS
The diagrams show how a simple motor works. When a current flows through the coil, a magnetic field is set up. The coil then has a north pole and a south pole as shown by the 'ghost' magnet drawn as though it were inside the coil. Permanent magnets give a magnetic field in which the coil turns. Forces of attraction and repulsion between the fields make the coil turn. As the coil turns *carbon brushes* rub against separate *commutator* segments to carry current to the coil as shown. When the poles of the coil are almost in line with the poles of the permanent magnet, the brushes are almost at the end of the commutator segments (1). But the moving coil cannot stop and carries on past this point. At the same time the commutator reverses the current flowing through the coil and in doing so reverses the poles of the coil (2). (This is shown in the diagram by the ghost magnet. The end with the black dot has changed from blue to red.) Forces of attraction and repulsion between the coil and the permanent magnet keep the coil turning (3) until the commutator changes the poles again (4). In this way the coil, or motor, keeps turning.

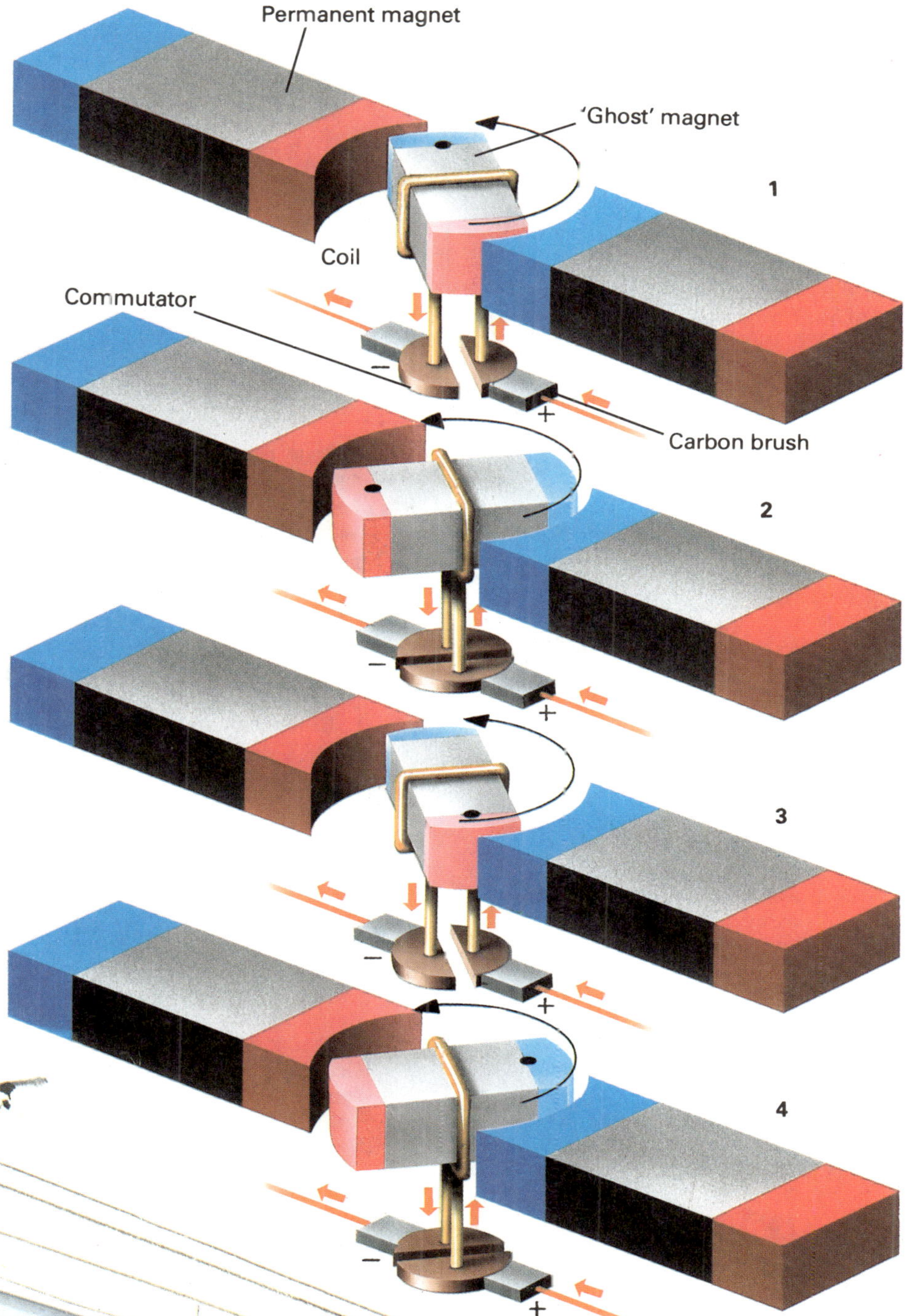

Great Inventions

The story of civilization can be traced in the inventions that Man has made. Among the early inventions of greatest importance were metal smelting, in the 4000s BC; the wheel and the plough, in the 3000s BC; and the harnessing of water power, in Roman times. But the pace of invention was slow until the 1400s, the time of the Renaissance, or 'rebirth of learning'.

1450	**Printing Press**	Johannes Gutenberg, Germany
1590	**Compound Microscope**	Zacharias Janssen, the Netherlands
1608/9	**Refracting Telescope**	Hans Lippershey, the Netherlands, and Galileo Galilei, Italy
1668	**Reflecting Telescope**	Isaac Newton, Britain
1698	**Steam Pump**	Thomas Savery, Britain
1712	**Beam Engine**	Thomas Newcomen, Britain
1733	**Flying Shuttle**	John Kay, Britain
1767	**Spinning Jenny**	James Hargreaves, Britain
1780s	**Improved Steam Engine**	James Watt, Britain
1783	**Hot-air Balloon**	Montgolfier Brothers, France
1785	**Power Loom**	Edmund Cartwright, Britain
1792	**Cotton Gin**	Eli Whitney, United States
1800	**Electric Battery**	Allessandro Volta, Italy
1800	**Lathe**	Henry Maudslay, Britain
1804	**Steam Locomotive**	Richard Trevithick, Britain
1815	**Safety Lamp**	Humphry Davy, Britain
1815	**Stethoscope**	René T. H. Laënec, France
1836	**Revolver**	Samuel Colt, United States
1837	**Telegraph**	William Cooke and Charles Wheatstone, Britain; Samuel Morse, United States
1839	**Steam Hammer**	James Nasmyth, Britain
1845	**Sewing Machine**	Elias Howe, United States
1856	**Bessemer Process**	Henry Bessemer, Britain
1867	**Dynamite**	Alfred Nobel, Sweden
1872	**Typewriter**	Christopher L. Scholes, United States
1876	**Telephone**	Alexander Graham Bell, United States
1877	**Phonograph (Gramophone)**	Thomas Alva Edison, United States
1878	**Cathode-Ray Tube**	William Crookes, Britain
1878/9	**Electric Lamp**	Joseph Swan, Britain, and Thomas Alva Edison, United States
1880s	**Machine Gun**	Hiram Stevens Maxim, United States
1884	**Steam Turbine**	Charles Algernon Parsons, Britain
1885	**Petrol Engine**	Karl Benz and Gottlieb Daimler, Germany
1888	**Pneumatic Tyre**	John Boyd Dunlop, Britain
1892	**Diesel Engine**	Rudolf Diesel, Germany
1895	**Radio**	Guglielmo Marconi, Italy
1903	**Powered Aircraft**	Wilbur and Orville Wright, United States
1926	**Television**	John Logie Baird, Britain, and Vladimir Zworykin, United States
1930	**Jet Engine**	Frank Whittle, Britain
1944	**Digital Computer**	Howard Aiken, United States
1947	**Polaroid Camera**	Edwin H. Land, United States
1955	**Hovercraft**	Christopher Cockerell, Britain
1971	**Microprocessor**	Intel Corporation, United States

Hot air balloon, 1783

The wheel was invented about 3000 BC

Motor cycle, 1885

The Wright brothers' 'Flyer'
The windmill was invented in Persia about AD 600
Telegraph, 1837
The bowdrill was invented about 50,000 years ago
Early telephone
Early TV tube
Early phonograph
Stephenson's Rocket, 1830
ROCKET
Early Scholes typewriter
Early Colt revolver

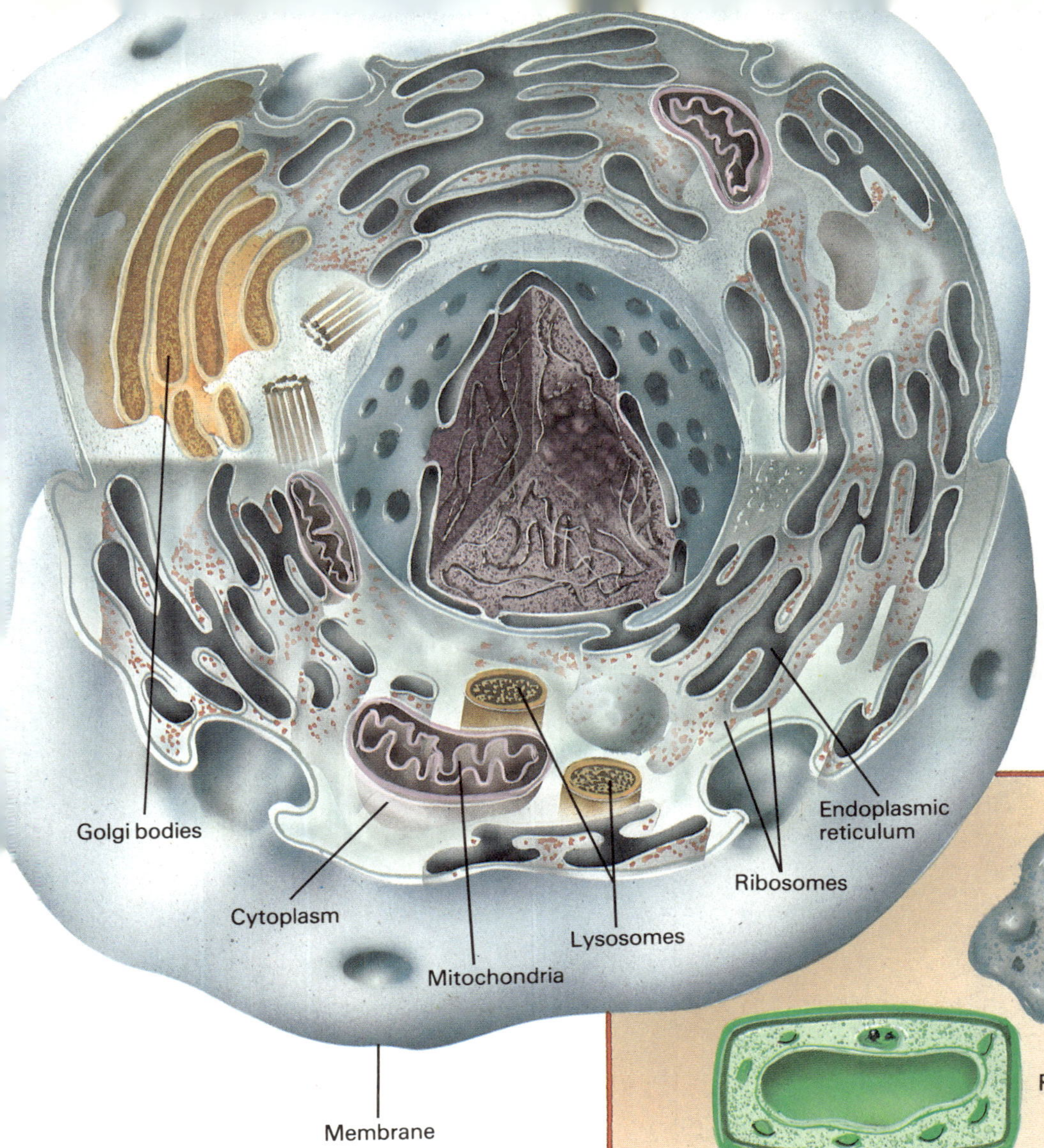

Parts of the Cell
The *membrane* is the cell's skin. It holds all the parts together.
The *cytoplasm* is all the inside of the cell except the nucleus.
The *nucleus* is the contol centre that orders all the cell's activities.
The *mitochondria* are the energy-producers of the cell. They take in food and give out energy for all the cell's parts.
Lysosomes are round bodies that break down the food that comes into the cell.
Golgi bodies are stacks of thin discs. Scientists are not sure what they do.
Ribosomes are dot-like objects that make proteins for the cell.
The *endoplasmic reticulum* is a channel that joins the cell's membrane to the membrane around the nucleus.

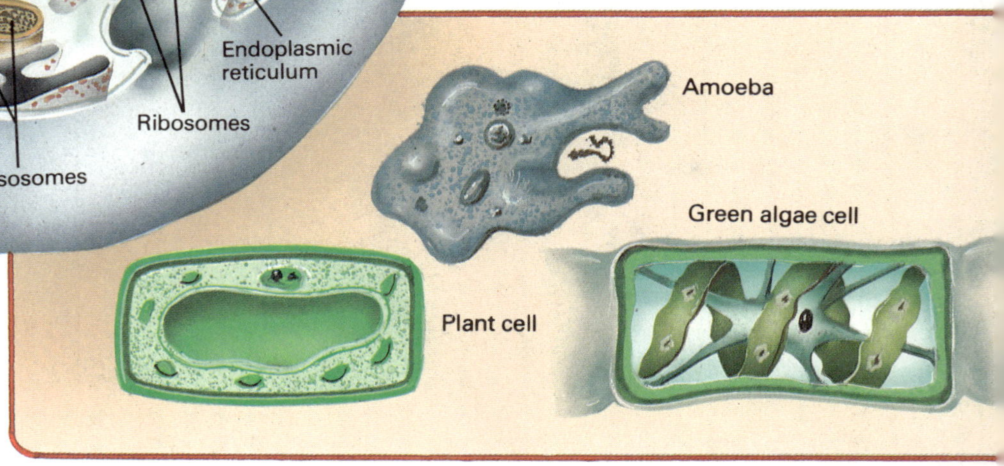

The Science of Life

Our bodies are made up of millions upon millions of tiny cells. All these cells grow from only two cells that join together at conception, when a new life begins. The cells come in all shapes and sizes. Some brain cells are only $\frac{1}{200}$ mm across. Other cells, such as muscle and nerve cells, are long and thin. Nerve cells can be as much as a metre long.

But all cells are similar in some ways. They are all enclosed in a thin membrane. Inside the membrane is the *cytoplasm*. This jelly-like stuff contains several different structures, and each has its own job to do. At the cell's centre is its *nucleus*. The nucleus is the cell's 'brain', controlling everything that the cell does.

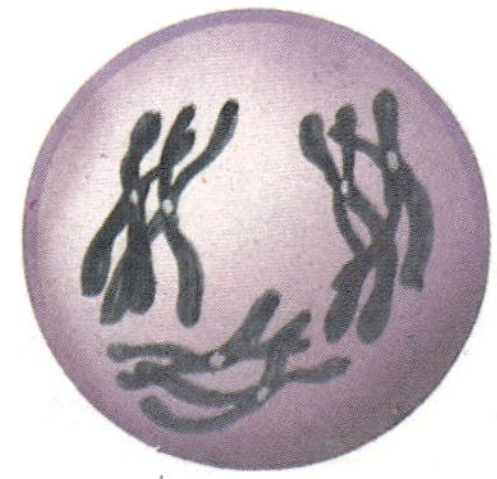

The nucleus is the cell's control room. Fine strands called *chromosomes* are scattered inside it. Chromosomes are made up of two kinds of substances – DNA and *proteins*. DNA is a chemical that controls all the things that are passed on from one generation to the next. It rules whether we will have fair or dark hair, blue eyes or brown. DNA does this by controlling the production of other substances called proteins.

Cells at Work

Below you can see some of the different kinds of living cells. *Red blood cells* are those that make our blood look red. They carry oxygen from the lungs all over our bodies. *White blood cells* are those that we need to protect us from disease. *Nerve cells* are shaped as they are so that they can carry messages to different parts of the body. *Lymphocytes* and *phagocytes* are two kinds of cell which 'eat' harmful bacteria in the body. When we cut ourself, bacteria often attack the wound. Then phagocytes come along and attack and surround the bacteria. If the invading bacteria or micro-organisms are still not beaten, the lymphocytes come along and secrete *antibodies* that make the invaders harmless.

Amoebas are tiny creatures that consist of only one cell. All the machinery for life is held inside them. Despite their small size, they are able to move about, feed themselves and reproduce.

Passing On the Information
A new life begins when two cells join to make a new one. This new cell must have in it all the characteristics that a person inherits from his or her parents. The cell must also contain all the information needed to build up a human body.

Each chromosome in the cell's nucleus is a chain of things called *genes.* There may be 1000 of them on each chromosome. The genes govern our hair colour, eye colour and all our other characteristics. The genes are made of DNA. Each DNA molecule is arranged in two spirals linked by chemicals, rather like the rungs of a ladder (see below). There are only four different chemical rungs but they can be arranged in a huge variety of combinations to give all the different characteristics that people have.

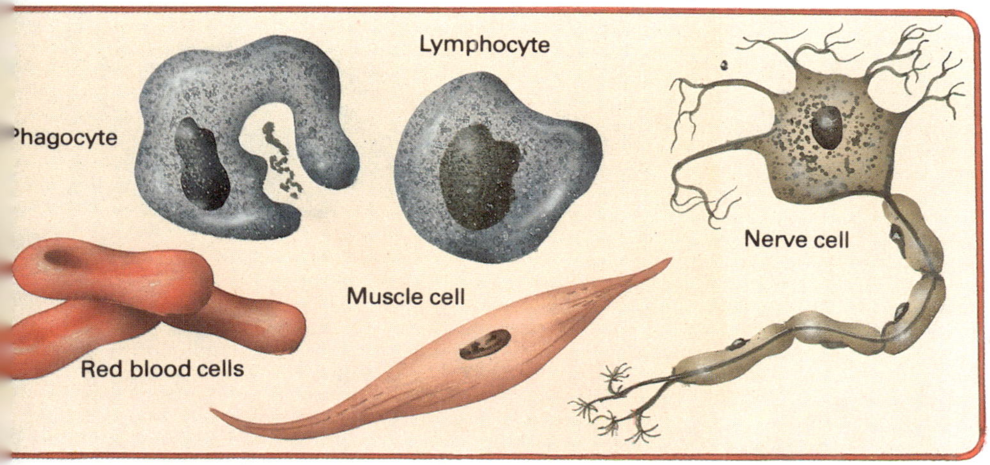

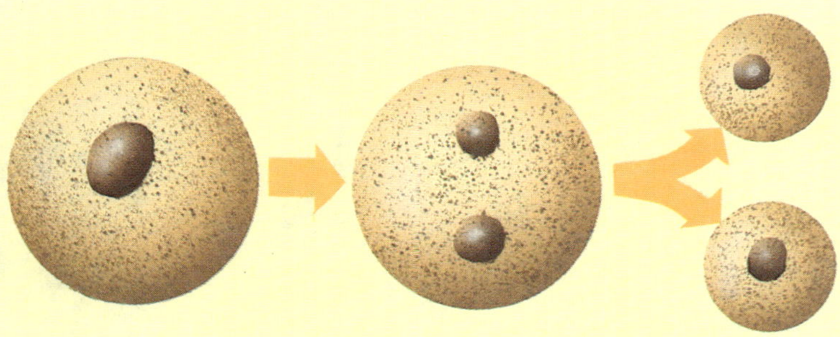

Making New Cells
The only way new tissue can be formed is from the division of cells. The nucleus splits in half to make two identical nuclei, each with a full set of chromosomes. Then the cell itself divides to make two cells.

There is another kind of cell division which takes place in *sex* cells. In this process, the parent sex cell, male or female, divides in such a way that each new cell has only half the number of chromosomes of the parent cell. So when the sex cells meet, each gives a half set of chromosomes to the new cell, which must therefore have a complete set of chromosomes, half from the father and half from the mother.

Science in the Home

Science has played a big part in making our homes comfortable and easy to operate. Even forgetting such things as television sets, radios, refrigerators and food mixers, there are many other ways in which science works for us. Many of the home inventions of the past hundred years are now so much a part of our daily lives that we seldom stop to think about them. The first canned food, for example, went on sale in the 1820s. But it was not until the 1860s that the first can-opener was invented. Before then, people opened cans with a hammer and chisel!

Cleaning and washing used to be hard work, often needing servants armed with mops and brooms. Then science came to our aid. The carpet sweeper was invented in

It is very seldom we have to think about all the wires, pipes and tanks that are hidden behind the walls, under the floors and in the lofts of our homes. Some of them are shown in the picture below. The big tank feeds all the water pipes throughout the house. The smaller tanks are fed from it and are for the hot water system. The hot water boiler on the ground floor may use gas, coal or oil to heat the water. The electricity supply comes in through a main fuse box. You can see how the wires run from a fuse through all the electric sockets in a room back to the fuse box.

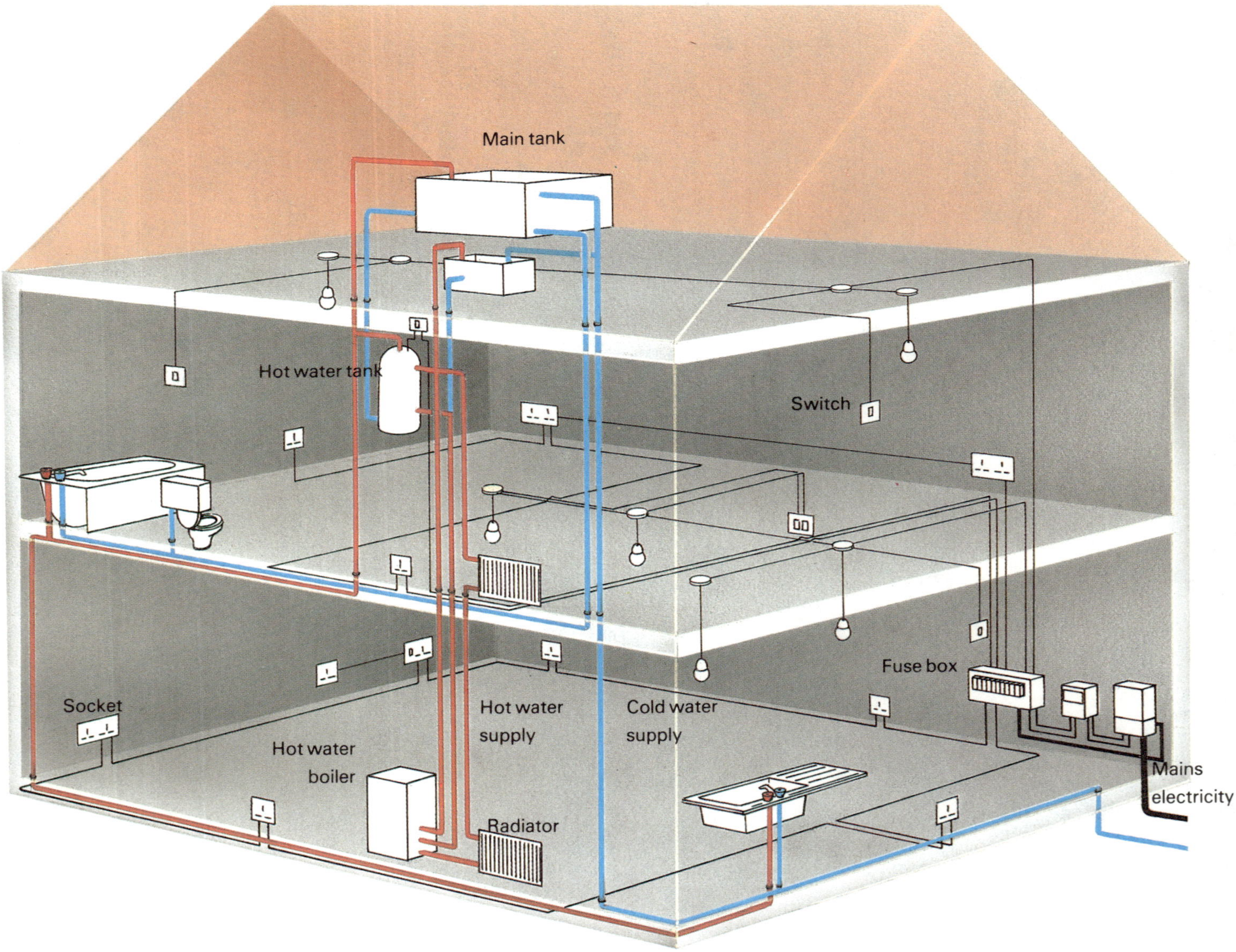

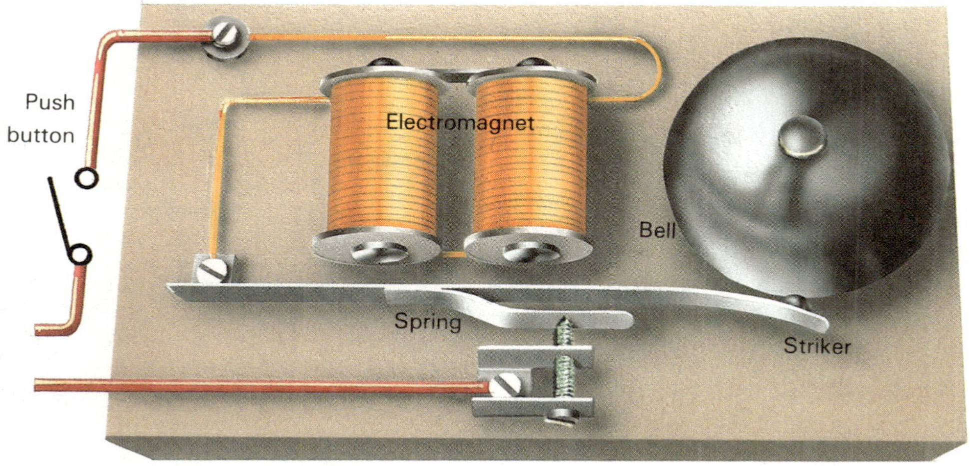

THE ELECTRIC BELL
When you press the button of an electric bell you close a switch that makes an electric current flow through an electromagnet. This magnetism moves a striker which hits the bell. As the striker moves, it opens the contact that passes current to the electromagnet. There is no magnetism, so a spring pulls the striker back. This closes the contact again and current passes again to the electromagnet. The bell rings and opens the contact again. In this way, the bell keeps on ringing as long as the button is pressed.

1876, soon followed by the hand-cranked vacuum cleaner, worked by bellows. In 1901 an electric motor and an air filter turned it into the vacuum cleaner.

The first washing machines were also worked by turning a handle. By 1914, electric motors were being used. Although detergents were invented as long ago as 1916, it was not until 1945 that they came into general use.

The oil lamp, like the candle, was one of the earliest and most useful inventions. Then came gas in the early 1800s. But gas light was rather poor until the invention of the incandescent mantle in 1885. The mantle was a sleeve of fine cotton soaked in chemicals. This fitted over the gas flame and burned to increase and spread the light. The carbon-filament electric lamp, invented around 1878, was the forerunner of today's tungsten-filament lamp and the fluorescent tube. Many other inventions, big and small, help to make our lives easier; things like safety pins, zip fasteners, sewing machines, safety razors, water closets and non-stick frying pans.

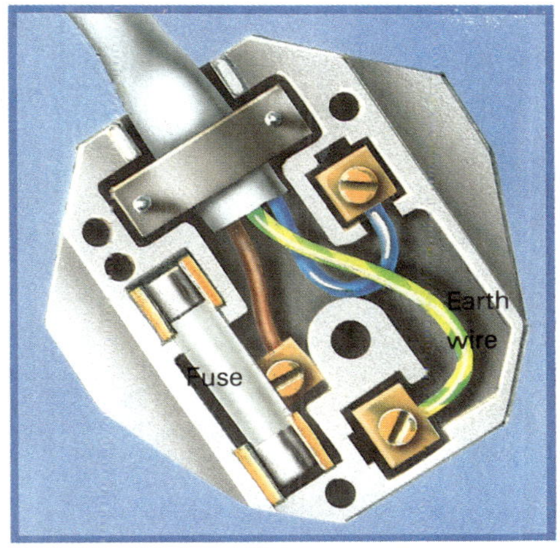

Electric plugs (above) should have a fuse inside them for safety. Inside the tube is a thin wire which melts if too much current passes through it. This cuts off the electricity before any damage is done. Without a fuse, an electrical fault could cause the current to rise and cause overheating and start a fire. Fuses are graded in amperes (amps) – an amp is the unit of electric current. The number of amps printed on a fuse is the amount of current that the fuse will allow through to whatever appliance is being used without 'blowing'.

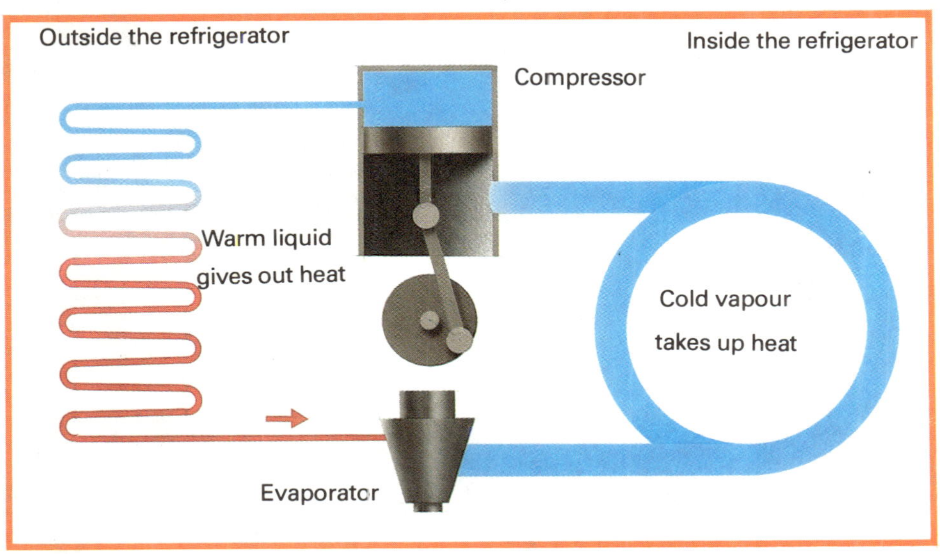

A refrigerator has pipes inside it that contain a cold fluid. This fluid easily changes from a liquid to a vapour. As it goes into the refrigerator it is liquid and is pumped through an evaporator. This lowers the liquid's pressure and it becomes vapour. The change from liquid to vapour makes the vapour cold. This cold vapour flows through pipes inside the refrigerator. After it leaves, it goes to a condenser. This increases its pressure and it changes back to liquid, giving out heat. In this way, heat is taken from inside the refrigerator to the outside.

Science in the Air

The cockpit of a modern airliner is a mass of electronics. A dazzling variety of dials and warning lights face the pilot. They keep him informed as to how all the plane's systems are working, whether he is on course and so on.

As the aircraft approaches an airport an Instrument Landing System guides it in. Ground control supplies the pilot with direction of approach. Aircraft usually start to line up with the runway about 7 to 10 kilometres from the airport; then they follow radio beams until they land. Landing has become more and more automatic, and many aircraft can now land without the pilot touching the controls at all.

Despite all these electronic aids, aircraft still need pilots. In passenger planes, two sets of all essential equipment are carried, in case one fails. But even if both sets fail, the air crew are still there to bring the plane safely to land.

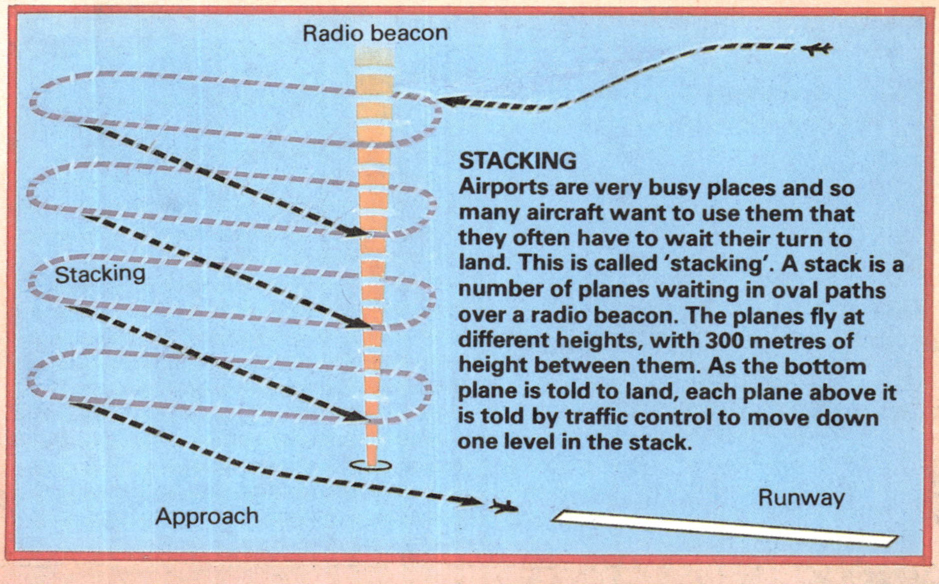

STACKING
Airports are very busy places and so many aircraft want to use them that they often have to wait their turn to land. This is called 'stacking'. A stack is a number of planes waiting in oval paths over a radio beacon. The planes fly at different heights, with 300 metres of height between them. As the bottom plane is told to land, each plane above it is told by traffic control to move down one level in the stack.

THE ALTIMETER
The pressure altimeter (opposite) tells the pilot how high he is above sea level. In the instrument is a sealed thin metal capsule filled with air. The pressure inside the capsule is always the same. But as the plane goes higher, the air pressure around it grows less. The air in the capsule can then push the thin metal outward. This turns a lever which works a pointer. Pipes connect the altimeter to the air outside the plane.

AEROFOILS
To fly, an aircraft must in some way lift itself off the ground against the pull of the Earth's gravity. This lift is produced by air flowing over the plane's wings. The wings have a special shape called an *aerofoil.* They are curved at the top and flat at the bottom. This means that the air passing over the top of the wing has to travel faster because it has further to go. So the air pressure is less above the wing than below it and the wing is lifted upward.

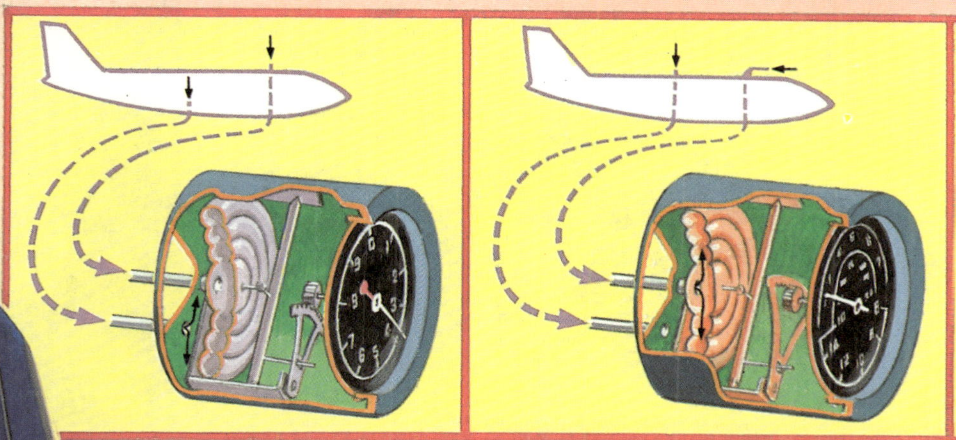

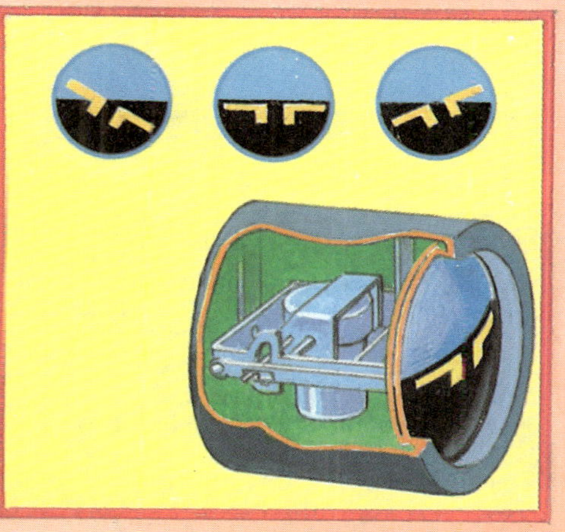

THE AIR SPEED INDICATOR

The air speed indicator is a most important instrument. It works by measuring the difference between the air pressure at the front of the plane and at the side. The faster the plane goes, the greater the difference in pressure. This difference is shown on a dial in the cockpit. The front air pressure is measured by air coming into a special *pitot tube* that sticks out into the airstream.

THE ARTIFICIAL HORIZON

This is an instrument that tells the pilot whether the plane is flying level. Inside is a gyroscope that spins at high speed and stays level with the horizon no matter what the plane does. The pilot can tell what bank, climb or dive the plane is in by a glance at the artificial horizon.

The pilot can change the shape of the wings by using 'flaps'. Part of the trailing edge and often the leading edge too can be hinged downwards. This gives more lift at lower speeds when taking off and landing.

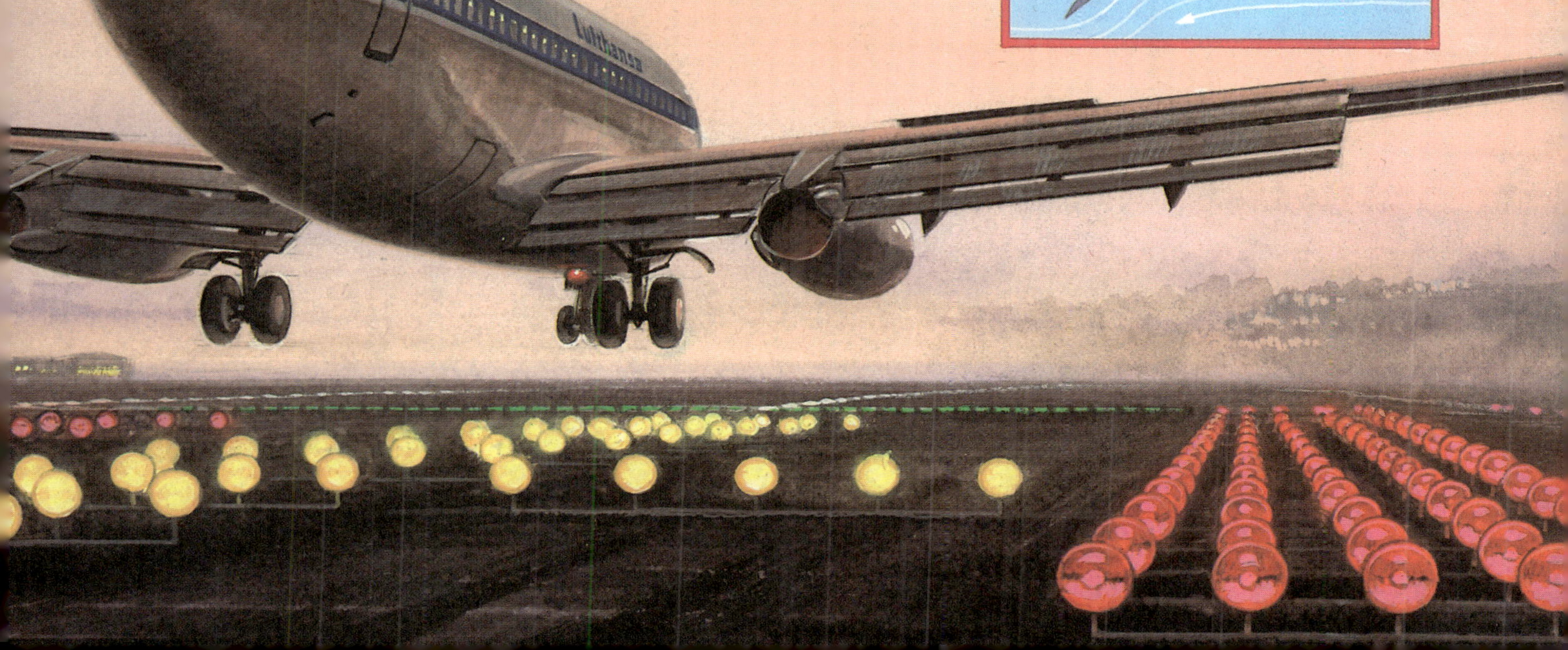

Under the Sea

Our Earth is the only planet in the Solar System that has oceans. And over three-quarters of its surface is water. For many centuries people have been diving down into the sea to hunt for things like sponges and pearls. The early divers plunged in and held their breath. Today, science is helping people to explore more and more of the great under-sea world. We are slowly finding out its secrets and beginning to extract its wealth.

But exploring the sea-bottom isn't easy. The average depth of the oceans is about 4,000 metres, with vast under-sea mountains and deep valleys. Only very special boats or unmanned vehicles can go down this far.

The oceans contain many substances that we need. There are vast deposits of metal ores on the Continental Shelf close to our shores. There are cricket-ball-sized lumps of the useful metals copper, nickel, manganese and cobalt lying on the deep-sea floors. But dredging useful quantities of these treasures has still to be achieved.

Lumps of minerals called *nodules* lie on the ocean floor as much as 5000 metres below the surface. In the future, special dredgers may be lowered to gather the modules. The dredgers will carry powerful lights and be guided by television cameras from the surface ship.

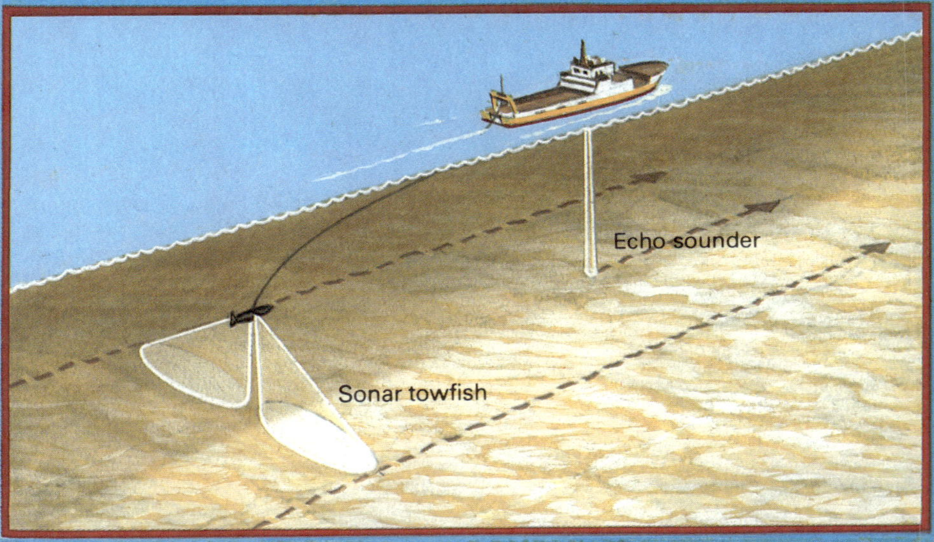

Sonar is used to find out what the sea-bed is like. One way of doing this is to tow a metal 'fish' behind the survey ship. The sonar equipment in the fish gives a picture of the sea-bed. An echo sounder on the mother ship draws a graph of the depth.

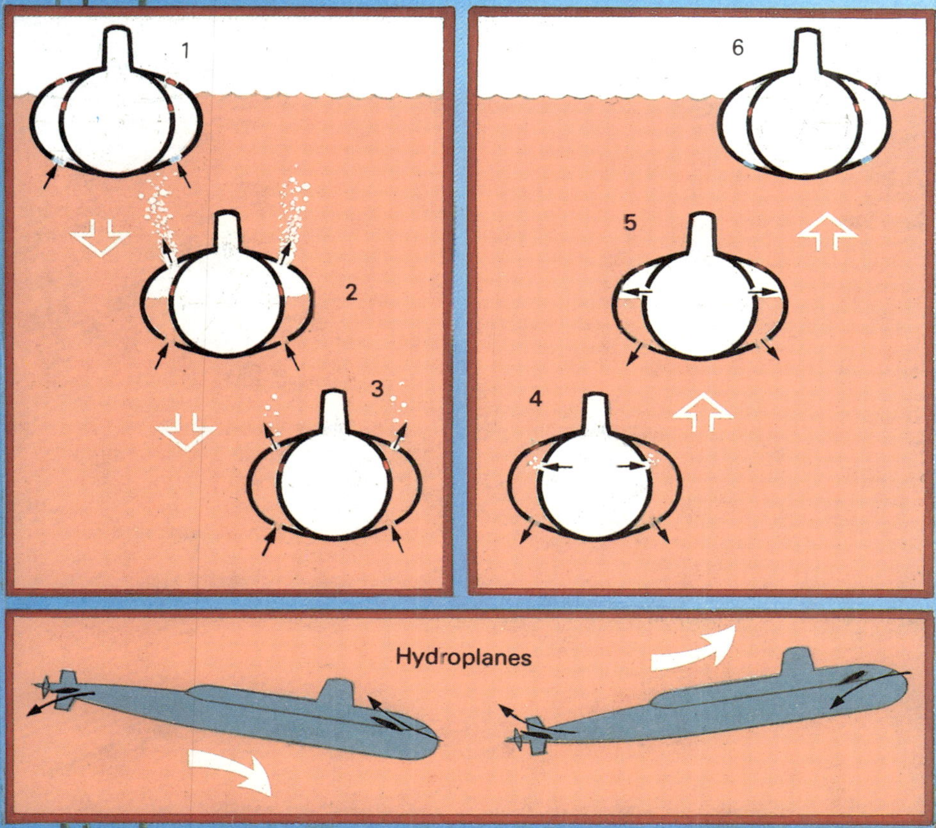

HOW A SUBMARINE WORKS

On the surface, a submarine's main ballast tanks are empty (1). To make it dive, water is allowed into the tanks (2 and 3). To make the submarine rise to the surface, pumps blow air into the tanks, forcing the water out (4). At the surface, fresh air is pumped into the tanks (5 and 6). But a submarine must also be able to manoeuvre under water. In addition to its main ballast tanks, it has smaller 'trim' tanks. Water can be allowed into or pumped out of these tanks to keep the vessel on an even keel when submerged. To dive or climb, the navigator uses hydroplanes which are rather like an aircraft's tail elevators.

Many submersibles are now at work beneath the sea. Some are scientific research vessels. Others are designed for underwater rescue operations. But the greatest demand for submersibles is in the undersea oilfields where they play a vital role in the inspection and repair of underwater oil installations.

Heat Engines

An engine is any machine that takes energy from heat, water or wind and makes this energy do useful work. The windmill and the waterwheel are simple kinds of engine, and people are still trying to make these engines more efficient. Steam engines took the place of the windmill and the waterwheel, and today we have petrol engines, diesel engines, jet engines and turbines.

A steam engine is a *heat engine*. Heat from burning coal, oil or gas is used to turn water in a boiler into steam. When water boils to become steam it expands to about 1,700 times its size. Steam engines use the energy of expanding steam to drive wheels or do other work.

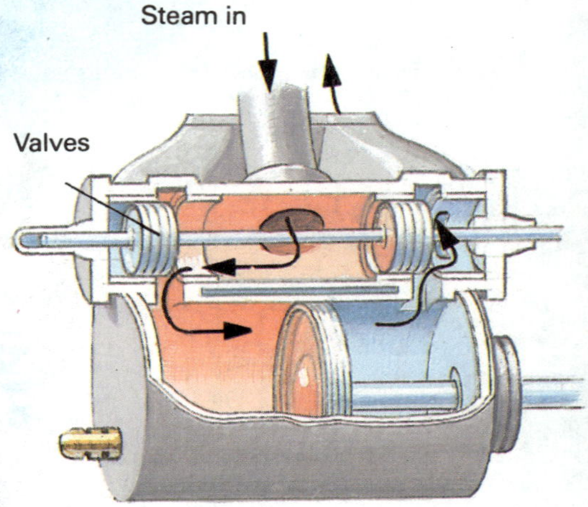

In a simple steam engine a piston slides to and fro inside a hollow cylinder. A system of valves allows steam into the cylinder at one end, then at the other, driving the piston back and forth.

How a Steam Engine Works
In a steam engine, the expanding steam pushes a piston to and fro inside a tube called a cylinder. The piston is attached to a piston rod that moves in and out with the piston. The piston rod is attached to another, longer rod called the connecting rod, which is joined to a driving wheel and makes it go round.

Various systems of valves allow the steam to shoot into the cylinder so that it drives the piston first one way, then the other. This kind of engine is called a *reciprocating* engine. At the beginning of the 1900s the reciprocating engine was the chief source of power. It ran locomotives, ships, factory machines and even motor cars. Today it has almost vanished because more efficient kinds of engines have been invented.

Another kind of steam engine is the *steam turbine*. A turbine is a large wheel with dozens of blades round it. A powerful jet of steam is made to hit the blades and cause the turbine to spin. Spinning turbines can be used to make electricity or drive a ship's propellers.

Internal Combustion
The motor car engine is called an *internal combustion* engine because the fuel is burned inside the engine. (In the steam engine the fuel is burned outside, away from the moving parts.) The internal combustion engine is more efficient than the steam engine. It gives more power for the energy put into it.

How it Works
The fuel – petrol or diesel oil – burns in a hollow cylinder. As the fuel turns to gas, it expands and

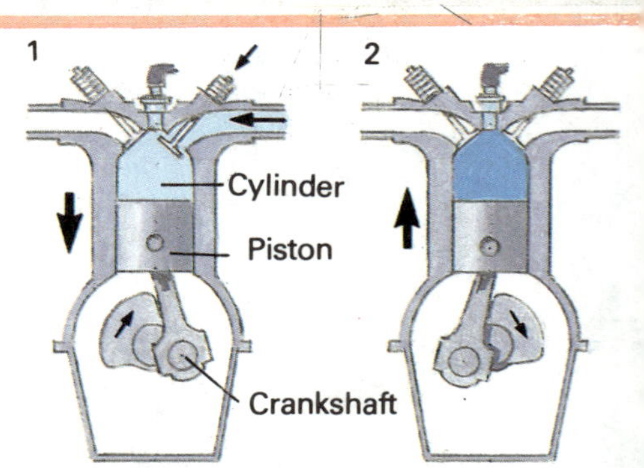

Petrol engines do not give power on every stroke of the piston. The diagrams above show what happens. At (1) an inlet valve opens and a mixture of petrol and air is sucked into the cylinder. Then the valve closes and as the piston goes pushes a tight-fitting piston down the cylinder. When the piston is pushed down, it turns a *crankshaft*. The crankshaft is made to turn the car's wheels.

The Wankel Engine

The Wankel engine is an internal combustion engine like the ordinary petrol engine, but there are no pistons moving in cylinders. Instead of pistons, the Wankel has a central rotor in the shape of a triangle with curved sides. As the rotor goes round the combustion chamber, the engine goes through the intake, compression, power and exhaust stages of an ordinary engine.

Jet Engines

There are several kinds of jet engine. The first to be invented, and still very much used, is the *turbojet*, pictured in the diagram below. It works by eating up air in enormous quantities – it needs the oxygen in the air to make the fuel burn properly. As air is sucked in at the front by a series of fast-spinning blades, it is *compressed* – squeezed into a small space. The air has to be compressed to give a lot of oxygen in the combustion chamber.

Special paraffin is sprayed into the combustion chamber. This fuel spray goes on all the time the engine is working. It is first ignited by electric sparks. As the fuel burns, its temperature rises to well over 1000°C. The hot gases expand and shoot out backwards into the atmosphere. This powerful stream of hot gas shooting out pushes the aircraft forward.

The hot gases turn another wheel called a *turbine*. A shaft connects the turbine to the compressor. This means that the compressor is kept turning and squeezing more air into the engine.

Jet speeds are sometimes increased by burning extra fuel between the turbine and the outlet nozzle. This is called *afterburning*.

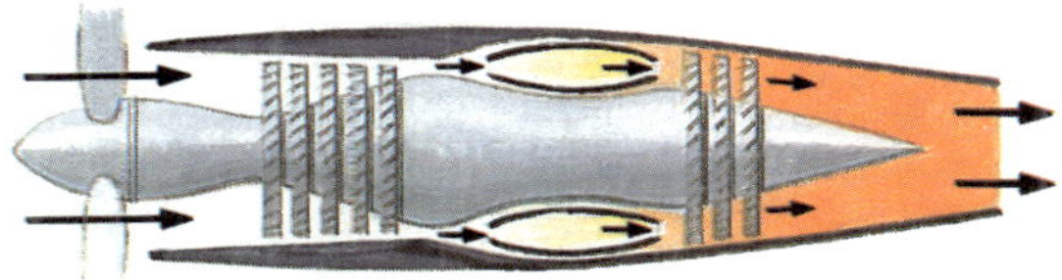

The engine above is a *turboprop*. In this engine the turbojet is used to turn a propeller which drives the aircraft forward. The turboprop is used on smaller aircraft, in which it is most efficient.

The *turbofan* engine pictured below is the one that powers most of today's big airliners. These engines have huge fans at the front to push enormous quantities of air back into the compressor. The air is divided into two streams; one goes through the combustion chamber, the other flows past the engine itself. The two streams combine at the back to give greater thrust.

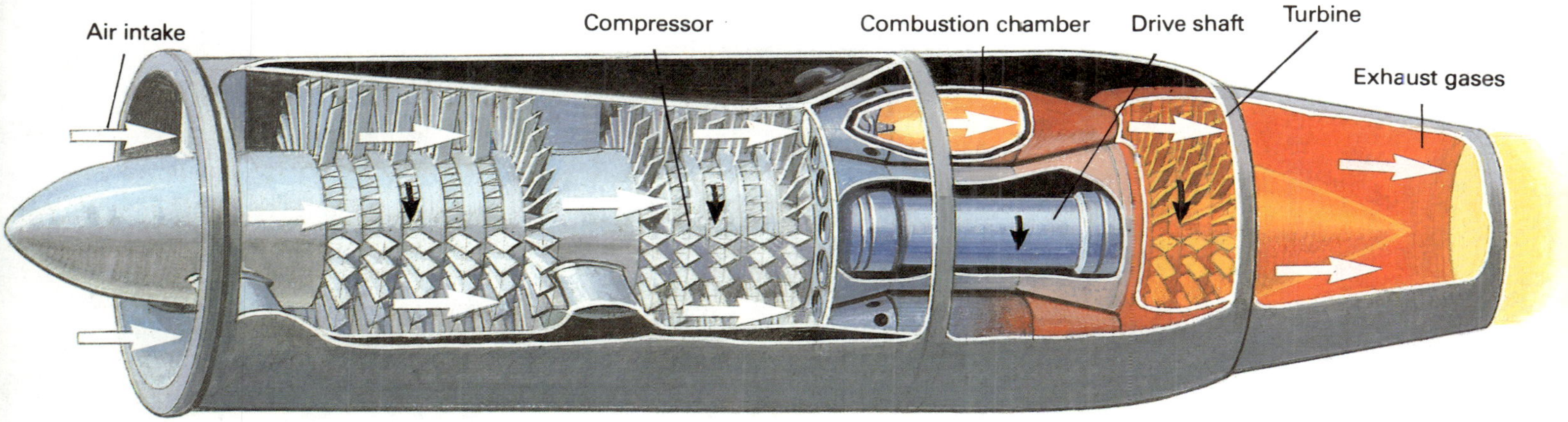

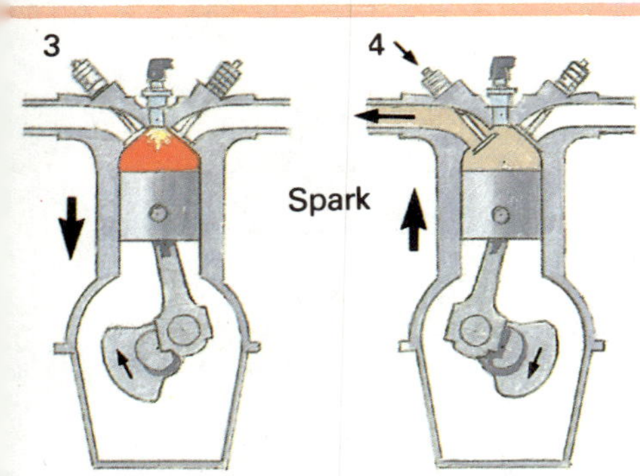

up it squeezes the fuel into the top of the cylinder (2). A spark takes place and the fuel mixture burns with great force and pushes the piston down the cylinder (3). Then an exhaust valve opens and the burnt gases are pushed out (4).

The Wankel engine

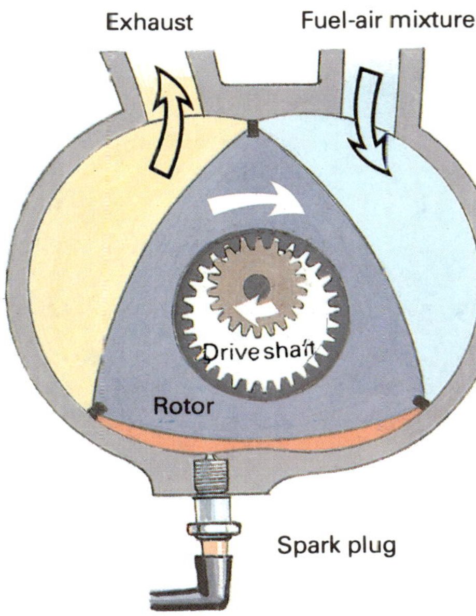

Radio and Television

Inside the Camera

The job of a television camera is to turn the image it sees into electrical signals that can be transmitted. In colour TV, the camera usually has three separate tubes inside it. These tubes split up the light from the image into three parts – a red part, a green part and a blue part. This splitting up is done by special mirrors called *dichroic mirrors*. You can see how this works in the diagram on the opposite page.

Each light colour goes through a special tube in the camera. These tubes make a pattern of electric charge as light falls on them. A beam of electrons in each tube moves quickly over the pattern of electric charge, going from left to right and top to bottom. This is called scanning. It makes a stream of electric signals, each signal telling how bright or dark a tiny part of the whole picture is.

From the Studio to Your Home

Several cameras are used to give different views of whatever is being televised. The cameras turn the image of what they see into electrical signals. These signals are fed to a control room where the programme director sits in front of a row of TV screens. Each screen shows the picture from one of the

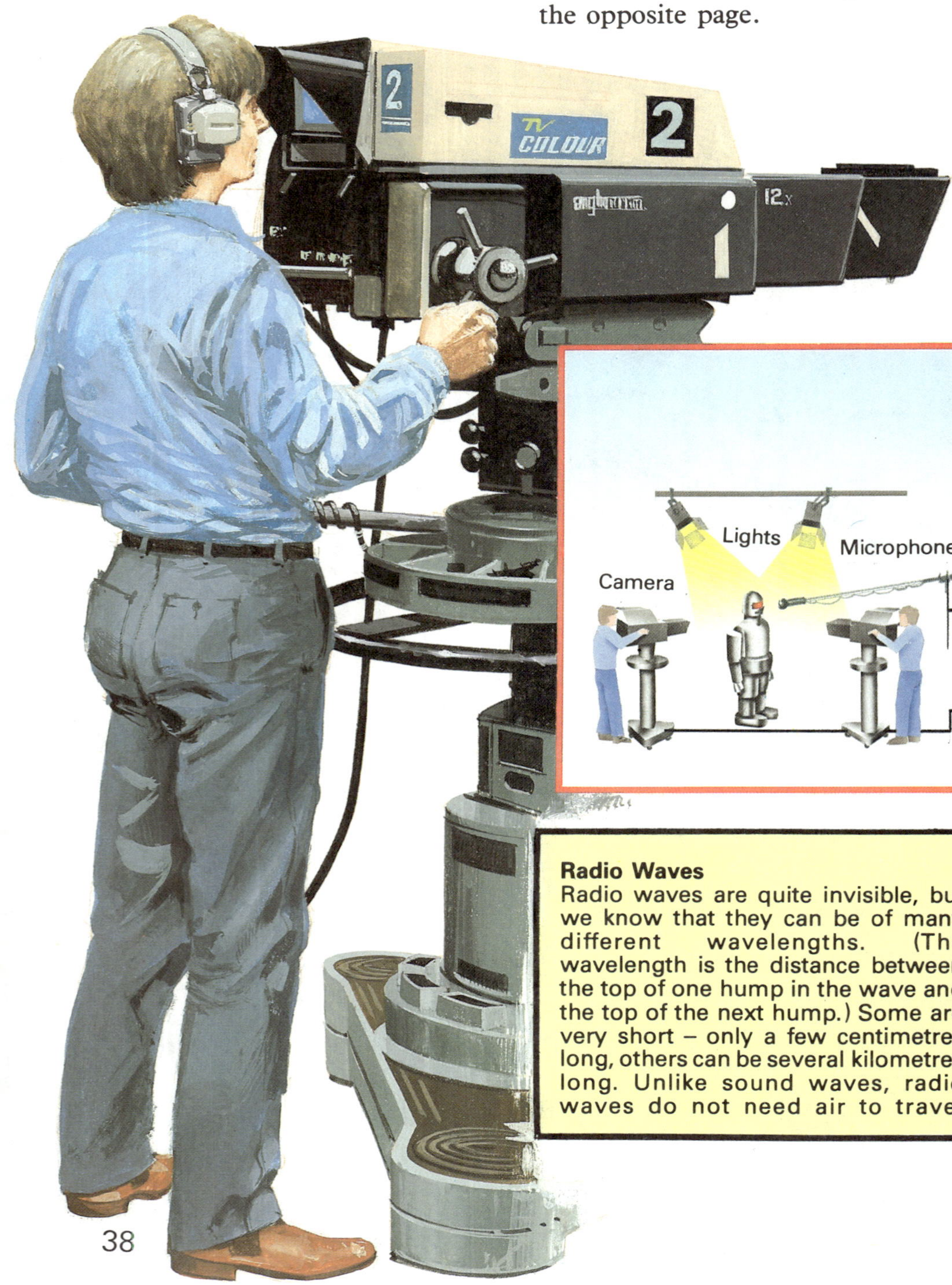

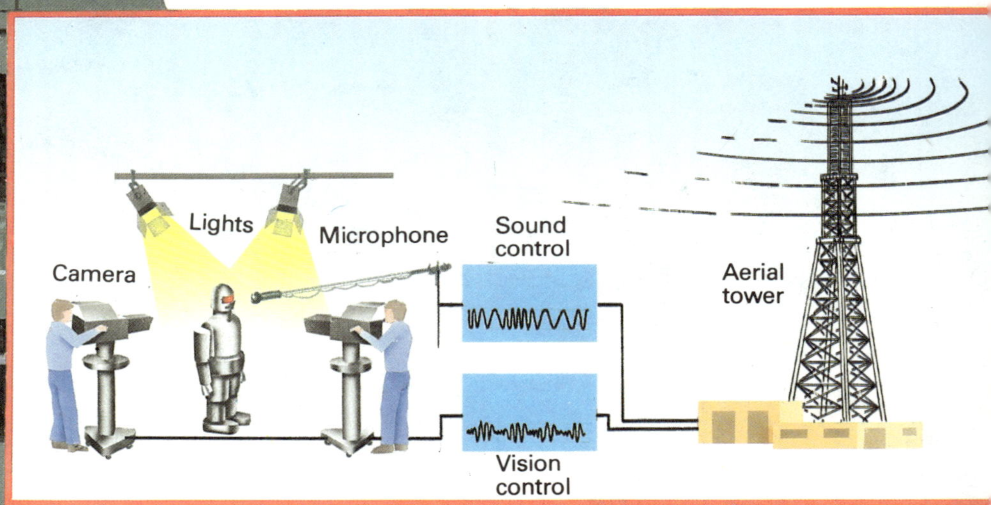

Radio Waves

Radio waves are quite invisible, but we know that they can be of many different wavelengths. (The wavelength is the distance between the top of one hump in the wave and the top of the next hump.) Some are very short – only a few centimetres long, others can be several kilometres long. Unlike sound waves, radio waves do not need air to travel through. We can talk to astronauts on the Moon because the radio waves travel quite easily through empty space. When a radio wave hits the aerial of your radio, it sets up a tiny electric current. If the set is tuned to the wavelength of the radio wave, the circuits in the set get rid of the carrier wave and send the signals of a person's voice or music to your loudspeaker.

cameras. The director chooses which picture he wants at a particular time, and the signals from this picture are fed to the transmitter. The transmitter may be quite a long way away from the studio.

Sound in the studio is picked up by microphones – again there can be several. The microphones turn the sound into electrical signals which go to a sound mixing position in the control room. There the sounds are selected or mixed as required before being fed to the transmitter.

The vision and sound signals are carried on radio waves sent out from the aerial at the top of the big tower. These radio waves are picked up by a receiving aerial and go into your TV set. The set turns the signals back into pictures and sound that you can see and hear.

Inside Your TV Set

When the picture signals go into your TV set they are removed from the radio wave that has carried them, and go into a cathode ray tube. You look at the front of this tube when you watch TV. An electron gun for each colour shoots out electrons which strike the back of the screen. This is covered with different types of tiny phosphor dots that glow blue, red or green when they are hit. The dots form the image you see.

Satellite TV

Orbiting satellites transmit television pictures world-wide.

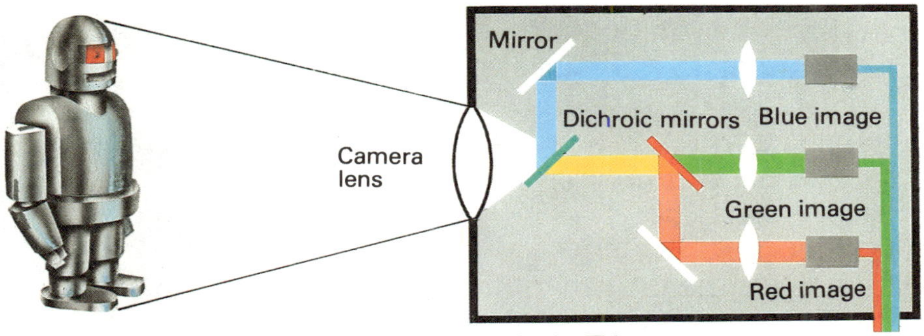

Inside the TV camera

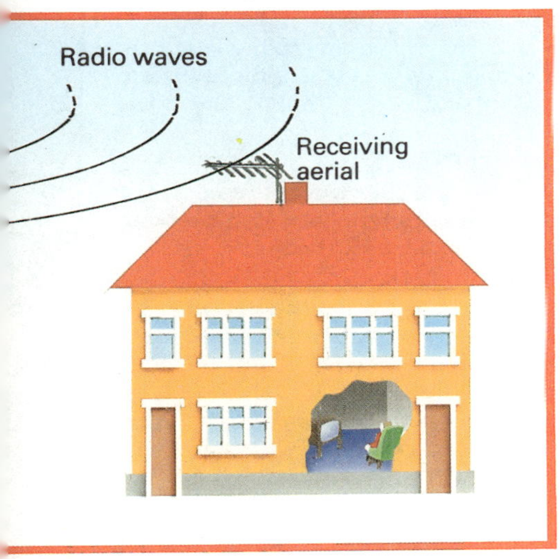

Red, green and blue dots form an image

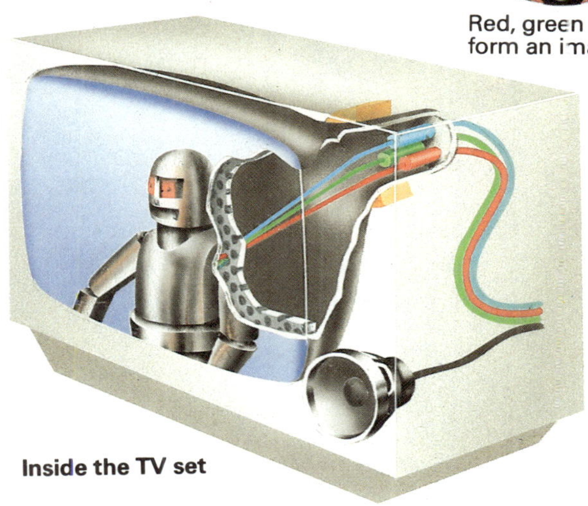
Inside the TV set

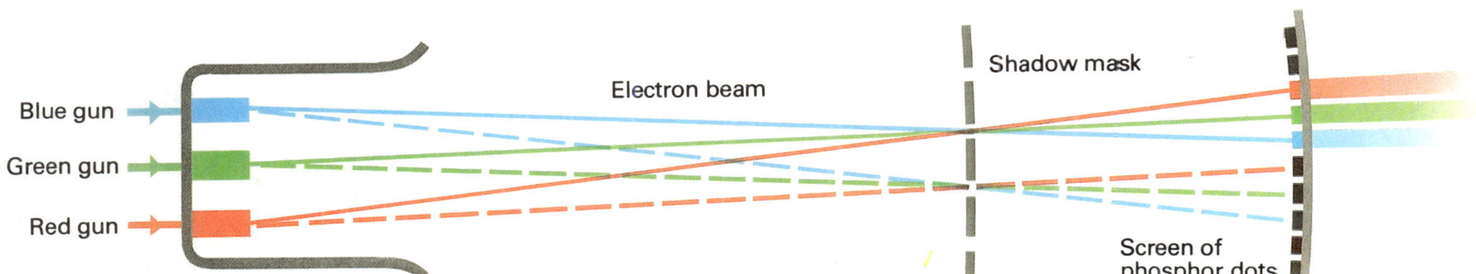

Inside the TV tube

Computers and Robots

Computers are playing a more and more important part in all our lives, whether we realize it or not. Businesses, large and small, are using computers to keep accounts, pay salaries, keep an eye on the stock position. They are used in schools, by the police, by banks, by the armed forces, by airlines and by scientists.

The strange thing is that computers can only do a few simple tasks. They can add. They can subtract. And they can compare one number with another. Why, then, are computers so special. The answer is that they can do these three things at lightning fast speed. They can do millions of calculations in a second.

Although the computer works with numbers, the information it uses does not have to start off as numbers. It can play chess with you, guide a spacecraft, check fingerprints and draw a map of Australia. But before it begins to work on any of these tasks it turns the information into numbers. And the numbers it uses are not quite the same as ours. We use the numbers 0 to 9. All the computer needs is 0 and 1. In fact, it can only count up to 1! This is called the *binary system*.

The computer uses the binary system because it has been designed to work with electrical currents. It can recognize the difference between a flow of current and no flow of current. If there is a current it registers 1; if there is no current it registers 0.

At the heart of every computer, pocket calculator or digital watch is the silicon chip. A tiny chip only 5 mm square, can be the main part of a computer. The number of microscopic transistors and other electrical parts that can be put on a chip has increased rapidly year by year. It is now possible to put more than a million of them on a single tiny chip.

Because the silicon chip is so small and cheap, computers have also become much smaller and cheaper.

As we press the computer's keys to give it commands, the computer translates our key commands into its own binary computer language and works on them. The result appears on the screen.

Communicating with the Computer

To instruct a computer to do something you have to write a program. Writing a program in binary numbers would take a lot of time and effort – the binary for our 8 is 1000 and to the computer the letter T is 01010100. So a simple solution has been found. The computer itself is programmed to translate our instructions into binary. We type in our program in a language we can understand. The computer then translates our language into its own language and starts work on it.

The computer does all its calculations in its main part – called the *central processing unit* or CPU for short. It also has a memory where it stores all the information that is fed into it. It stores little bits of information in separate memory locations or 'boxes'. All we have to do is give the computer the address of any memory location and the machine will find the information in that location in a millionth of a second.

To communicate with a computer we usually type in letters and numbers as on an ordinary typewriter, but using some special computer commands.

WHAT IS A ROBOT?

A robot is a machine that can be programmed to do different tasks. And most robots have an arm or arms that can do work for us. The robot's master is a computer.

More and more robots are working in factories all over the world. They spray paint, lift heavy loads and weld things together. And when they have been taught to do these things they usually do them better than human beings can. Switch on a robot and it will go on working 24 hours a day without stopping for a rest. It can work in places where people could not exist, and it hardly ever goes sick.

In the picture below, robots are welding cars as they move along an assembly line. Very careful programming lies behind a production system like this. A computer controls the robots so that they spot weld sections of each car without getting in each other's way.

Journeys into Space

Vostok 1 was the Russian one-man spacecraft in which Yuri Gagarin made the first ever manned flight into space (1). He blasted off on 12 April 1961.

The Americans who landed on the Moon travelled in *Apollo* craft (2). The Command Module for the men was in the nose of the spacecraft.

Venera 4 (3) was one of several Russian craft that reached Venus and released a capsule by parachute (right). The *Veneras* radioed back to Earth several important discoveries.

American *Pioneer* probes (4) flew close to Jupiter in 1973 and 1974. They took some remarkable close-up pictures of the giant planet.

A *Viking* Mars craft is seen at (5).

On March 16, 1926, an American scientist, Dr Robert Goddard, fired the first liquid-fuelled rocket into space. Goddard's rocket rose only 60 metres into the air, but this was the first tiny step towards bigger and more powerful rockets that took people to the Moon and probes right out of our Solar System.

A mere 31 years after Goddard's rocket, the Russians launched Sputnik 1, the first man-made satellite to orbit the Earth. This happened on October 4, 1957, and it was on that day that the Space Age began. Since then, hundreds of satellites have been fired into space and the Shuttle blasts off into space and lands back on Earth with an ease we are now beginning to take for granted.

Probes to the Planets

Some of the most exciting space projects have been the unmanned probes sent up to find out more about other planets in our Solar System. In 1976, two *Viking* spacecraft landed on Mars. They carried out tests to find out whether any form of life existed on the Red Planet; but they could find none.

Left: A *Voyager* space probe flying past Saturn's rings. in 1977 two *Voyagers* were sent to Jupiter, then on to Saturn. *Voyager 2* went on to Uranus and Neptune, sending back billions of images of the planets, before continuing its journey into deep space. *Voyager 2*'s signals from Uranus took two hours to cover the 2940 million kilometres to Earth!

The picture below shows the Space Shuttle with Spacelab in its cargo bay. Scientists will be able to work in Spacelab for up to a month.

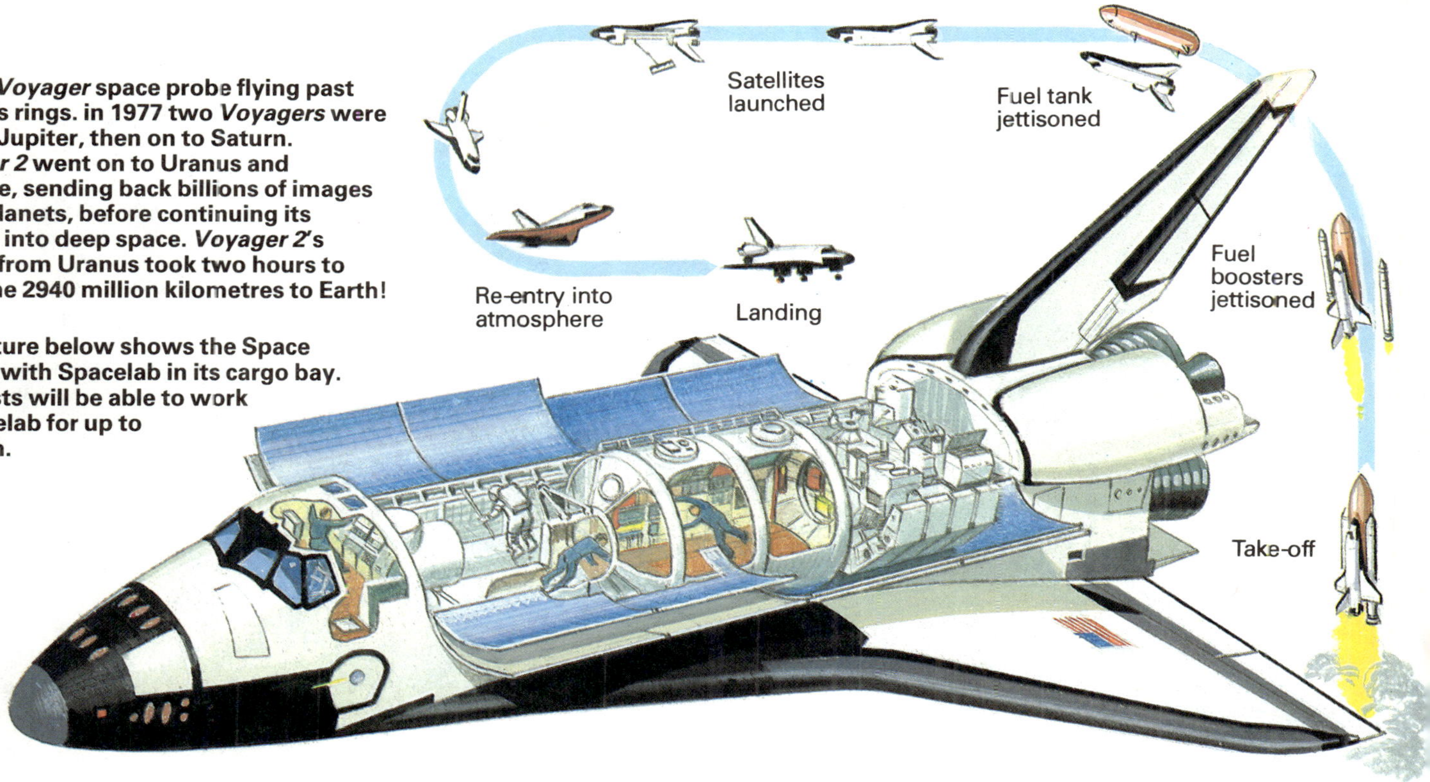

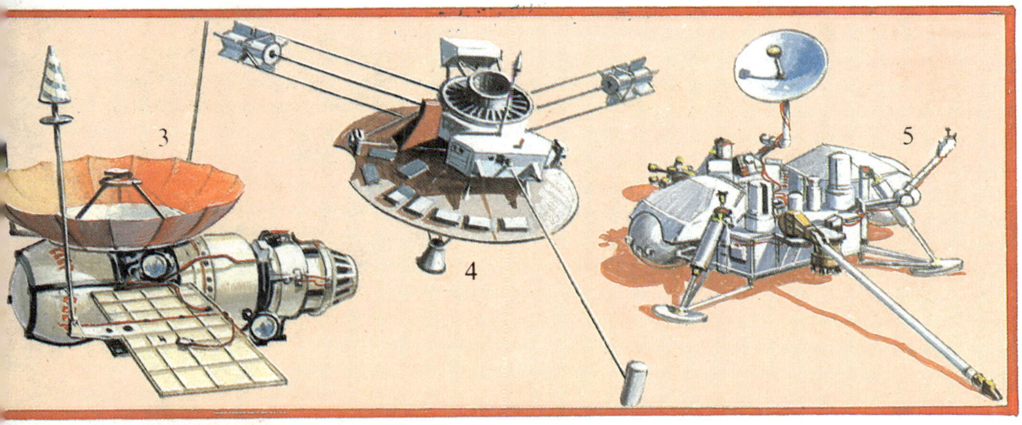

The Space Shuttle

When the Space Shuttle *Columbia* blasted off in 1981 a new kind of space travel began. After a flight of 54½ hours in space, it glided back to a perfect landing on a desert airstrip.

Before the Shuttle, all rockets and manned spacecraft were used only once. This made space flight very expensive. The Space Shuttle is a combined launch rocket and spacecraft that can be used many times.

The Shuttle is launched by rocket like other spacecraft, but it glides back to land on a runway like an aircraft. It has three main rocket engines which are fed with fuel from a big tank. This tank is dumped when all its fuel is gone. Two extra rockets are attached to the sides of the Shuttle to help it into space. These rockets fall away as the ship climbs, and drop by parachute into the ocean. There they are recovered and can be used again. As the Shuttle glides back through the atmosphere, special tiles protect it from the fierce heat.

Tomorrow's World

The world we live in is changing faster than ever before. The invention of robots and the microchip is bringing about a revolution in the industrial countries. In years to come people should have a better standard of living, better health, better education, and far more leisure time.

But there are many problems facing mankind in the future. There are many millions of people in the poorer countries who do not have enough to eat. Many cannot read or write and they have little medical care. It will take many years and much effort to make their lives anything like as comfortable as our own.

Below: As the Earth's supplies of metals run out it is possible that other planets and their moons will be mined. The metals will be refined in space and then brought back to Earth.

Bottom: There are many schemes to harness the energy of the waves. One scheme involves large tanks or 'ducks' being rocked up and down by the waves. The motion of the tanks would be used to drive an electricity generator.

In richer countries there are other problems. The consumption of energy and raw materials, for instance, is so great that the Earth is running short of many of its riches. Unless vast new oilfields are found the world will run out of gasoline within thirty years at the present rate of consumption. And the supply of certain metals such as copper and tin will last little longer. That is why scientists are searching for alternative sources of energy, such as harnessing the heat of the Sun and the motion of the waves. For the same reason the recycling of materials will become more important.

Above: The shape of tomorrow's transport is already on the drawing boards. The main feature of all the designs is that they will use as little energy as possible.

Below: In the future self-supporting colonies will probably be established in space. They may take the form of huge spinning rings. The spin would create artificial gravity for the colonists.

Index

Illustrators
Mike Atkinson, Jim Dugdale, Ron Jobson, Janos Marffy, John Marshall, Bernard Robinson, Frederick St. Ward, Mike Saunders and David Wright.

Cover illustrations by
Brian Watson/Linden Artists

 Published in Great Britain by Cliveden Press, an Egmont Company, Egmont House, PO Box 111, Great Ducie Street, Manchester M60 3BL.

Printed in Singapore.

ISBN 0 7498 0396 7

Reprinted 1992